D1241415

Cloak and Cipher

DAN TYLER MOORE
and MARTHA WALLER

Cloak and Cipher

BOBBS-MERRILL   Indianapolis   New York

Dedicated

To Betty and Mac

Library of Congress Catalog Card Number: 62-10008

Copyright © 1962 by The Bobbs-Merrill Company, Inc.
Printed in the United States of America
First Edition

THE **BOBBS-MERRILL** COMPANY, INC.
A SUBSIDIARY OF HOWARD W. SAMS & CO., INC.
Publishers • INDIANAPOLIS • NEW YORK

Contents

—The Magnet Hands You the Message—The Hollow Nickel—Colonel Abel—Triangulation —Black Tom Explosion—Pinpricks—Genghis Khan—The Ring That Can Hold Cipher Messages or Poison—The Concealment Belt—The Spy Camera—Camouflages—Sultan Ibrahim's Perfume Code

Cloak and Cipher

1. Death by Secret Writing

AT eight o'clock on the morning of February 8, 1587, a beautiful lady knelt down and placed her neck upon a block. The trembling executioner cut off her head with one stroke of his glittering ax. When he stooped to pick up the head, the witnesses gasped to see it roll away, leaving in his hand only a red wig, which the victim had worn because her own hair had turned thin and white during her long imprisonment. Such was the death of Mary, Queen of Scots, executed upon the order of Queen Elizabeth I of England.

Sir Francis Walsingham, the head of Elizabeth's small but efficient spy service, had intercepted some letters between the Scottish queen and a plotter, Anthony Babington. These letters were in secret writing. Unfortunately for Queen Mary, her secret-writing system was not secret enough. Walsingham figured out how to read the Babington letters, which proved that Mary, Queen of Scots, had been plotting to assassinate Queen Elizabeth. Since Mary was Elizabeth's cousin, and next in line to the English throne. Elizabeth's death would have made Mary mistress of both kingdoms. Elizabeth decided to strike first, and she signed the warrant for her rival's death.

It was not the ax that was responsible for Mary's death; she died of a fatal case of bad secret writing. Oddly enough, only a few months before her death, a French nobleman had published a book describing a secret-writing system that could have saved her life. (*See* Chapter 15.)

On September 17, 1813, one of the greatest battles in all history raged near the city of Leipzig, Germany, between the great general Napoleon Bonaparte, on one side, and most of the rest of Europe on the other. Historians refer to it as "The Battle of the Nations."

Napoleon, realizing that his opponents were too numerous for him, decided to withdraw his army across the Elster River. He sent back a letter in secret writing to Marshal Augereau, instructing him to come up from the rear and build bridges across the river for the planned withdrawal. The Marshal, using the same system of secret writing, replied immediately that his men had marched all night, were completely exhausted, and therefore would be delayed in building the bridges. He advised Napoleon to throw up emergency defenses to protect his army during the delay.

Marshal Augereau's letter reached Napoleon with its secret writing so badly garbled that it could not be read. Expecting him to arrive at any moment, Napoleon did not bother to throw up emergency earthworks. When the Marshal did not arrive, the Allies attacked and broke Napoleon's lines. They smashed his army, and, because there were no bridges, they were able to take over twenty thousand prisoners. Napoleon never really recovered from this terrible disaster.

Twenty-one months later, there occurred what many regard as the greatest battle in all history—the Battle of Waterloo. The Duke of Wellington, with an English army of only 67,655 men and 156 cannon, faced the Emperor Napoleon, the world's greatest general, who led a French army of 71,947 men and 246 cannon. It certainly looked bad for the English.

Napoleon was afraid that his old Prussian enemy, General Bluecher, would perform the impossible feat of arriving in time to help the English. The Emperor sent an urgent message in his "Great Cipher" to Marshal Grouchy, commanding another army of thirty thousand Frenchmen only a few miles to the southeast, to come quickly and join in the battle. The Emperor's message arrived, but, to quote the English historian Arnold Foster, "It was not understood." Grouchy marched off in the wrong direction, and Bluecher arrived with his Prussians to help the English defeat Napoleon.

Valor and the cannon of Waterloo defeated Napoleon, but, like Mary, Queen of Scots, the Emperor was already mortally ill from at least two bouts with bad secret writing.

At 9:45 on the morning of April 18, 1943, Admiral Isoroku Yamamoto, the Commander-in-Chief of the Imperial Japanese Fleet, leader of the attack on Pearl Harbor, and one of the top brains in Japan's war against the United States, was flying near the Island of Kahili in the South Pacific. A squadron of Japanese Zeros was guarding his plane. Suddenly, out of nowhere, appeared two squadrons of American Lightnings. They shot the Admiral out of the sky—one of the most dramatic and unexpected incidents of World War II.

The Japanese had hired a famous Polish cipher expert to devise a system of secret writing for them that no one could ever solve. However, cipher experts of the United States had cracked the Japanese naval cipher. They were able to read the secret Japanese radio messages, giving the route that Admiral Yamamoto's plane was taking. It was not only the incendiary bullets from the diving Lightnings that killed the architect of the "Day of Infamy." Like Mary, Queen of Scots, he died from a fatal case of bad secret writing.

Secret writing, with codes and ciphers, is almost as old as writing itself. History is full of the stories of kingdoms, armies, and people that have been destroyed by that fatal disease. Again and again, the story has been the same: the secret writing was not secret enough. Some enemy puzzled out the method, and was able to uncover the secret.

Most of the ciphers of history have been simple substitutions, like the one used by Julius Caesar. For every letter in the alphabet, Caesar substituted the one three letters further on. Using our modern alphabet, his famous message, *Veni, vidi, vici* (I came, I saw, I conquered), would appear as "Yhql, ylgl, ylfl."

A simple substitution cipher appears in the Bible (Jeremiah XXV:26). Because he wanted to keep the word "Babylon" secret in one of his prophecies, Jeremiah switched the letters in the Hebrew word for Babylon, and got the word "Sheshach."

There is just one thing wrong with such a simple substitution cipher—it is too simple to be safe. Such a method of secret writing should never be used in an important message. It can be solved by almost anyone who has a little time to work on it. (See Chapter 12 for an explanation of the method.)   ,

A simple substitution cipher does not conceal vital information. Such systems can always be solved. One need only know, as Edgar Allan Poe demonstrates in "The Gold Bug," that in the English language the letter most frequently used is E. The next is T, and then come O, A, N, I, R, S, H, B, L, and F, in that order.

2. How Secret Writing Makes History

In the fall of 1618, just two years before the Pilgrim Fathers landed in America, Louis XIII, the King of France, and his great adviser, Cardinal Richelieu, were fighting for their lives against the French nobles. It was the era when Dumas's famous heroes, the Three Musketeers, wielded their swords. The King's great general, Prince Condé, was trying to capture the City of Réalmont. Unless he took it quickly, the King's position would be seriously damaged. The Prince, however, dared not risk an attack because his army was small and the city was reputed to be heavily defended.

While Prince Condé was puzzling over this problem, a messenger was caught sneaking out of Réalmont with a letter. In it was a poem so atrociously worded that the sophisticated Prince decided it must be some sort of a cipher. He was perfectly right, but neither the baffled Prince nor the frustrated members of his staff were able to decipher it.

Finally, in desperation, the Prince sent for Antoine Rossignol, a French mathematician who lived nearby, and asked if he could read the letter. Rossignol, working with frantic haste, found that the poem had been enciphered, or put into secret writing, by a method known as the "Cardan Grill." He finally unscrambled the meaning from the mishmash of third-rate poetry. This one letter changed the whole balance of power between the French King and his nobles. The letter was actually an appeal for help from the defenders of Réalmont, who complained that their city had no weapons with which to defend itself.

The astonished Prince Condé ordered a herald to approach the walls of Réalmont with a loud blast of bugles. The herald carried not only the secret letter, but also Rossignol's solution of the secret writing. The horrified defenders immediately surrendered their city to the French King.

Antoine Rossignol went on to become one of the greatest cryptographic geniuses of all time. His uncanny ability to read the secret writings of all the other kings and nobles in the world was one of the greatest assets of that most powerful of all French kings, Louis XIV.

Under Louis XIII and his grandson, Louis XIV, the French nobles were reduced from dangerous war lords to harmless courtiers. Time after time, due to the uncanny skill of Rossignol, the French nobles fell victims to that most fatal and subtle of all maladies, bad secret writing.

Rossignol was as clever at making up secret writing as he was in deciphering it. He made sure that no one could read the secret letters of his master, King Louis XIV. The Great Cipher that he invented was so secure that, after the King's death, its secret was lost. Although the greatest cryptographers of following generations tried to read the hundreds of letters that had been written in it, the Great Cipher withstood all their efforts for two hundred and seventy years. Its secret was finally unraveled by the great French cipher expert,

Bazeries, in 1890. The Great Cipher was a cryptographic horror, in which hundreds of characters were substituted for various syllables and words of the French language.

Rossignol was also the discoverer of the most important law of secret writing: "A secret message must be safe enough so that by the time the enemy gets it solved, it is too late to be of aid to him." Everyone who uses secret writing should remember this law.

Someone who did not remember it was James Scott, Duke of Monmouth, who decided in 1685 to drive his uncle, King James II, from the English throne. On Monmouth's side was the most powerful noble in Scotland, the Duke of Argyle. They started communicating with each other and with their followers in a complicated type of secret writing in which, if the reader took only the first letters of certain of the words in a message, the real meaning came out.

The two dukes, with their fleets, finally attacked simultaneously—the Duke of Argyle on the west coast of Scotland, and the Duke of Monmouth on the west coat of England. To their consternation, the soldiers of the English King were ready and waiting for them to land. Both dukes were captured, and King James had their heads cut off.

The King's agents had intercepted their letters and had figured out their secret-writing system. Although the two powerful dukes died under the ax of the executioner, what actually killed them was that old bugaboo, bad secret writing.

Two hundred and sixty years later, during World War II, there was a story going around the Office of Strategic Services (the United States spy service) about an English traitor, Harry Ordway (the name is fictitious). Ordway moved back and forth between the German and American armies tipping off each to the other's artillery movements, and getting well paid by both sides. He was what is sometimes referred to as a "free-lance double spy."

Once, when Ordway was reporting to a representative of the OSS, the American agent said, "Your information is getting so valuable, Ordway, that we really should pay you what it is worth. I'm going to give you a letter of introduction to Sir William, the head of British Force 145, and he will take care of your compensation." The American quickly wrote out a message for the delighted double spy to carry to Sir William:

SIR HARRY ORDWAY OFTEN TELLS THINGS HELPFUL IN SOLVING MOVEMENTS ARTILLERY. NECESSARY ARRANGE TERMS OF NEW COMPENSATION EMPLOYMENT.

The double spy presented the letter to Sir William, who read it carefully, and then rang a buzzer. A squad of men filed into the room. "Seize this man," ordered Sir William. "Take him out into the compound and shoot him."

The traitor struggled to escape. "I don't understand!" he shouted.

Sir William stared him down. "I think you do understand," he said. "You would understand more, however, if you had read only the first letter of each word of the note you brought. You are, of course, a double agent. The wages of a double agent when he is caught are always the same . . . death."

3. Transposition Ciphers

THE word "cipher" comes from the Arabic word *sifr*, which has also given "zero" to our language. Cipher is also related to the Hebrew *sathar* (figure).

The message sent to Sir William shows one way in which a cipher can be made. Although separated by the harmless words of the "cover" message, each letter has kept its own identity.

In secret writing, whenever letters retain their own identities (A being really A, B being B, et cetera) but are separated from each other, transposed, or mixed up in their order, the cipher is called a "transposition." When writing was first invented, there was no need for ciphers, since the letters or hieroglyphs were so mysterious that only a handful of people could read them. But twenty-three hundred years ago, when the Persian Empire was in a temporary period of peace with Greece, there were plenty of people who could read Greek, so the Spartans invented the first system of transposition to safeguard their secret communications.

A slave who had journeyed hundreds of miles through enemy

territory from Sparta to Byzantium arrived in Sestos, where the Spartan leader, Lysander, was encamped. He had been stopped and searched many times, but was allowed to proceed with his harmless letter to the Spartan ruler.

When he arrived, Lysander showed no interest in the letter. Ordering everyone from the room, he asked the astonished slave for his colorfully-decorated belt. He thrust one end of the belt into a hole in his Commander's baton, then twisted the belt around the baton in a tight spiral so that the edges touched.

The jumble of letters on the belt, which looked like a religious charm, sprang into words and sentences when read down the length of the baton. To his horror, Lysander learned that his "friends," the Persians, were really his enemies, and that they were hatching a plot against him in Sparta preparatory to taking over the city. Lysander rushed his army back to Sparta by forced marches and smashed the plot. The *scytale* (rhymes with Italy), the oldest-known type of transposition cipher, had saved Greece from the barbarians.

It is easy to use this type of cipher. A bottle, a can, a stick, even a pen or pencil of a convenient diameter may serve the secret purpose of Lysander's baton (*See* Photos 1, 2, and 3). The strip of paper on which the message is written can be attached satisfactorily with cellophane tape. It is not difficult for someone who knows the method to figure out the meaning, with or without a special stick. He can wrap the strip around a cone to see where the letters come together as words. This will indicate the diameter of the "baton" to which the message is keyed. As cryptographers say, this type of cipher has "low security," but it was good enough to fool the Persians, and it will still fool many people.

A modern refinement of the *scytale* involves the use of thread instead of a strip of leather or paper. When the thread is wrapped tightly and evenly around a cylinder, a message can be written on the tightly-wound thread with a fountain pen. If the thread is soaked in alum before it is used, the ink will not run.

To construct a transposition cipher of the *scytale* type, cut a narrow strip of paper, ten or eleven inches long, about the shape of the one shown in Photo 1, and wrap it around a Spartan general's baton. If none is available, use a standard six-sided pencil as a *scytale,* and fasten the paper strip on both ends with Scotch tape, as in Photo 2. Now write a message in print down the length of the pencil, and write lines of unrelated letters down the other five sides of the pencil, as shown in Photos 2 and 3. When the paper strip is removed, it appears to be covered with gibberish, as in Photo 1. To decipher it, the recipient must wrap it around a pencil of identical diameter.

Almost any object can be used as a *scytale,* the only require-

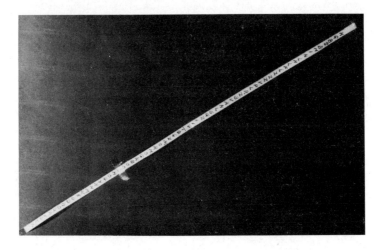

PHOTO 1. *Finished message of a pencil scytale*

ment being that there is by prearrangement an identical object at both the sending and the receiving end. Glasses, vases,

PHOTO 2. *Pencil scytale*

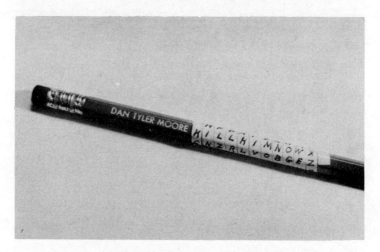

PHOTO 3. *Pencil scytale fastened with scotch tape*

books, and boxes have all been used as *scytales*. Ungummed Western-Union teleprinter tape five-sixteenths of an inch wide is perfect for wrapping around a *scytale*. It can be purchased at twenty cents per roll.

There are many other ways in which letters can be scrambled or transposed to form secret writing. Even simpler than the *scytale* is writing in reverse. Thus I LOVE YOU becomes UOY EVOL I. Reversed writing has the advantage of speed. Some people find that they can write almost as rapidly in this cipher as they can in plain language. One helpful trick is to use a mirror for writing or reading in reverse; the eye works from left to right and the mirror reverses the image. Care must be taken that the letters themselves are not reversed along with the order. Я in place of R would give away the game at once. Like the *scytale*, reversed writing is of very low security.

Another quick method of jumbling the letters of a message is to split them apart like this:

I O E O

L V Y U

On one line, I LOVE YOU then becomes IOEOLVYU. This is known as the "rail-fence" cipher. Simple as this system is, it was used as late as the American Civil War.

Much safer types of transposition are the "route," "columnar," and "grill." The names suggest the methods used for rearranging the letters. When a message is enciphered by a route transposition, it is inscribed or written inside a rectangle of prearranged size on graph paper. (See FIG. 1.) If the message is too short to fill the "box," it may be padded out with "nulls," or meaningless letters. If the message is too long, a second box is used, and the process repeated. The letters are then read off in some definite pattern.

A	T	T	A
C	K	A	T
D	A	W	N

FIG. 1. *Single transposition cipher*

If the message ATTACK AT DAWN is inscribed in a three-by-four box (See FIG. 1), the cipher may be produced in a variety of ways, depending upon which route is chosen for reading off the letters. For instance, beginning in the lower left corner and reading alternately up and down the columns, the message becomes DCATKAWATATN. A more complicated route produces NWTAAADKTCTA as the enciphered form of the same message. Beginning with N in the lower right corner, the sender moves left to the adjacent letter W and proceeds diagonally from lower left to upper right. Instead of doubling back at the end of the diagonal, he shifts at once to the base line and proceeds with the letter to the left of the one wih which his previous diagonal began. As used by spies or by armies, route transpositions usually involve a larger box and a longer message. The variety of possible routes is almost endless.

If the lines of the message are read off vertically instead of horizontally, another kind of cipher, "columnar transposition," is produced. The secret writing then is ACDTKATAWATN. This provides little security, but the next trick is to alter the order in which the columns are read. A key word provides the order:

Key: T O R E
         4 2 3 1

A T T A

C K A T

D A W N

Using TORE as the key, the cryptographer sets up the order as based on the relative position in the alphabet of the letters in the key. Since E comes earlier in the alphabet than T, O, or R, the E column is read off first, followed by the columns under O, R, and T, in the same order in which they appear in the alphabet. The message now reads ATNTKATAWACD.

If a cipher is to be used at all extensively, it should be economical, using only as many letters as the original message, or at least twice as many. If, as is so often the case, the secret is a matter of life and death, the cipher must also be secure enough to fit Rossignol's rule—too difficult for the enemy to break in time to do him any good. The simple transposition ciphers are economical, but a cipher expert can usually read them, especially if the message is short.

How does he do this? The letters themselves show the same *frequency* as plain language. That is to say, there will be the same percentages of A's or B's, Q's or Z's that there would be in any plain message of the same length. The cipher expert, or cryptanalyst, as he is properly called, knows the common combinations, and, perhaps, can even guess a likely word. If there are two U's and one Q, for instance, it is a certainty that one of the U's must follow the Q. Using the knack of the Scrabble player, the expert works the letters into words. Always on the alert for hints as to the nature of the basic pattern, he eventually can detect the entire system.

This recombining of letters to form words is called "anagramming." It was once a popular pastime. Writers delighted in concealing their own identities, or those of their enemies, in anagrams. Such an author was Prosper Mérimée, best remembered for *Carmen*, his tale of the gypsy girl and the bull fighter. Early in his writing career, Mérimée published a collections of plays in French, which he claimed were translations from the work of a fictitious señorita, whom he called Clara Gazul. The frontispiece was a picture of Mérimée himself, fetchingly draped in a mantilla. Since foreign books were then the rage of Paris, this bit of deception stirred public interest and undoubtedly made the book more successful than it might have been had Mérimée admitted it as his own work. Later, a volume of Illyrian folk ballads appeared under the title *La Guzla*. A *guzla* is a stringed instrument, but a few alert readers noticed that *guzla* is also an anagram of "Gazul" and guessed correctly that the two books were the work of the same man.

Anagramming has also been used to promote religious and political views. Presbyterians, for example, have been delighted to find that the word PRESBYTERIAN can be shuffled into BEST IN PRAYER.

One of the most unpopular measures ever taken by the American government was the Embargo of 1807, which for-

W	E	W	I	L	L	H
A	V	E	T	H	E	S
E	C	R	E	T	M	E
E	T	I	N	G	I	N
T	H	E	C	A	V	E
U	N	D	E	R	T	H
E	B	R	I	D	G	E

FIG. 2. *Simple rectangular transposition*

bade the import and export of all goods to and from Great Britain. Opponents of this policy switched the letters of EMBARGO to GO BAR 'EM, O GRAB ME, and MOB RAGE. In the election of 1936, a Republican anagram fan pointed out that the letters of the Democratic nominee's name, FRANKLIN DELANO ROOSEVELT, could be converted into a slogan for the other candidate: VOTE FOR LANDON ERE ALL SINK!

We will close this chapter with a quick exercise in rectangular transposition. To encipher the message, "We will have the secret meeting in the cave under the bridge," as a simple rectangular transposition, write the message in a square horizontally, as in FIG. 2. Then remove the letters vertically and place them in groups of five:

WAEET UEEVC THNBW

ERIED RITEN CEILH

TGARD LEMIV TGHSE NEHE

To decipher the message, the recipient must put the letters back vertically into the square and read them horizontally.

4. More Transpositions

ON February 17, 1880, the Winter Palace of Tsar Alexander II of Russia was rocked by an explosion that destroyed the imperial dining room and killed thirty people. This was one of many acts of terrorism of a type that had become all too common. A secret society, the Nihilists, had pledged themselves to destroy every vestige of government in the country.

Although the intelligent and fair-minded Tsar had given freedom to Russia's millions of serfs, Alexander himself was the Nihilists' prime target. Once an assassin barely missed him with a pistol shot. Then twenty people died when a train on which he was thought to be traveling was dynamited.

The police seemed powerless to stop the Nihilists. Nothing daunted, Alexander called a committee to draft a constitution that would make Russia a democratic monarchy. At the same time, he reorganized the secret police under the leadership of the clever General Loris Melikoff, who set out to destroy the Nihilists by boring from within—insinuating his own spies into the terrorist organization.

Through the work of these agents, Melikoff caught two ring-

33

leaders of the Nihilist conspiracy. One of them revealed that the organization had enlisted the services of an explosives expert for a major project and also that the other prisoner, Mikhailoff, was connected with the publication of secret newspapers.

Melikoff was anxious to discover the location of the Nihilists' printing presses. One of Mikhailoff's guards was instructed to appear sympathetic to the terrorists' aims, while another was allowed to furnish him with pen and paper. Melikoff did not have long to wait. Mikhailoff wrote a long letter, which he "persuaded" the friendly guard to deliver to his Nihilist friends.

The letter was written in cipher. However, that did not trouble Melikoff, some of whose staff had taken cryptographic training in the German government's excellent laboratories. The secret message proved to be an editorial, in the usual Nihilist vein, on the miseries of the working class. Having studied it, Melikoff allowed it to be forwarded to the secret newspaper headquarters.

Several more letters of the same sort followed the same route. The imperial police discovered the location of the secret printing presses and made dozens of arrests. To their disquietude, however, they also discovered that another plot to kill the Tsar was about to be carried out. Two organizations could play at the game of boring from within: one of the Nihilists arrested was a man in the police department.

On the very day, March 13, 1881, on which the new constitution was signed, Alexander II set out to review the Imperial Guard. A section of the street behind him suddenly blew up. Two of the Tsar's Cossack guards were killed and several others wounded. Instead of fleeing in terror, the courageous Tsar turned back. As he bent over one of the injured men, another charge exploded and the man who wanted to make Russia a democracy was mortally wounded.

From that day on, Russia was full of ominous portents. The murdered Tsar's son, Alexander III, tried to reestablish absolute power, and a grandson, Nicholas II, eldest son of Alexander III, was dogged with tragedy from the time he ascended the throne. Three thousand people were crushed to death when the reviewing stands collapsed in the confusion of his coronation; the imperial chain broke and fell during the ceremony; at his marriage—so soon after his father's death that the court was still in deep mourning—his bride wore a black veil. The reign that began so strangely would end in a cellar, where the Tsar and all his family would be massacred by their Communist guards.

Our relations with Russia today might be very different if the imperial police had been better at cracking ciphers in 1881. Good cryptanalysis might have saved the able and intelligent Alexander II from his assassins. If Melikoff's staff had been wise enough to look beneath the first cipher for a second one, concealed within the routine propaganda they uncovered in Mikhailoff's messages, they would have learned that it was actually Mikhailoff himself who had plotted the Tsar's assassination from his prison cell. He had used a cipher within a cipher to give the Nihilists plotters detailed instructions for their crowning act of terror. He was smart enough to guess that if the letter were to fall into the hands of the police, they would be satisfied that they had obtained the whole message once they had cracked the first cipher.

A little knowledge of cryptanalysis is a dangerous thing. If Melikoff's staff had been really brilliant, they could have changed the course of history. If, on the other hand, they had been too stupid to read the first Nihilist cipher of Mikhailoff's messages, ironically, they would have saved the Tsar—because they would have put a stop to all further communication.

The second—inner—cipher of Mikhailoff's messages was a

biliteral form of the variety described in Chapter 28. The messages in the first cipher, which Melikoff's police could and did read, were conveyed by an elaborate transposition known as the Nihilist Cipher. A message in this system is produced by inscribing the letters BLOW UP BRIDGE in a box, like those of the previous chapter:

	key:	T	O	R	E
		4	2	3	1
Row 1		B	L	O	W
Row 2		U	P	B	R
Row 3		I	D	G	E

Instead of reading them off by a route, the cryptographer puts the letters together in this order: first, the letter in Row 1, Column 1 is W; then Row 1, Column 2 is L, and so forth until the row is finished. Then comes Row 2, Column 1, which is R; Row 2, Column 2, which is P, and so forth, until the message is completed. BLOW UP BRIDGE enciphered with the keyword TORE in the Nihilist Cipher is WLOBRPBUEDGI.

The Nihilist cipher alone was secure enough to fool many police forces in Europe. An even better transposition is achieved by taking WLOBRPBUEDGI and repeating the columnar method a second time. "Double Columnar" proved to be so safe that it was used in the German Army in World War I. However, sending and receiving messages in this type of cipher is such a painstaking process, that one wonders if eyestrain contributed to the final German defeat.

There is no doubt that anyone who looks at such a message knows at once that it is secret writing. Rather than be caught with anything obviously incriminating on his person, a spy often prefers to conceal a dangerous message in a seemingly innocent cover letter by the use of a "grill." Although there are many varieties, the simplest kind of grill is a sheet of paper with certain cut-out squares or spaces. When the spy composes his letter, he first lays the grill over a plain paper and writes the words of his message through the holes. Then he fills out the paper with other words to form what appears to be a casual letter about his family's health or the neighborhood doings. The agent who receives the letter has an identically perforated grill, which he lays over the letter to reveal its secret meaning.

The defenders of Réalmont used such a grill, with a cover of such rotten poetry that the King's men smelled a cipher. The perforated grill is supposed to have been the invention of Jerome Cardan, one of the greatest physicians and mathematicians of the Renaissance. On one occasion, Cardan apparently flabbergasted the theological world by daring to cast a horoscope for Jesus Christ.

A more sophisticated type of grill than Cardan's, and one that has been used for military purposes in modern times, is made by cutting a pattern of holes in a square sheet of coordinate paper. (See FIG. 3.) One-fourth of the squares are perforated. The first quarter of the message is written through the holes on a sheet of paper beneath it. Then the grill is rotated ninety degrees, or turned so that one of its sides is at the bottom. Then the second quarter of the message may be inscribed. The process is repeated until the whole message, or the largest possible section of it, has been written and the final quarter has been used. If the message is shorter than the grill, meaningless letters called *nulls* may be used to fill the empty spaces. If the message is longer than the grill, the process of inscription and rotation is repeated the necessary number of times. If the grill is properly constructed and used,

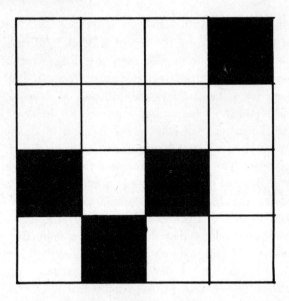

FIG. 3. *Rotating grill*

no spaces are left blank or exposed twice, and every letter except the nulls contributes to the message.

Unlike a message made with a Cardan grill, which uses words, one made with the rotating grill (letters) is obviously in cipher. The Cardan grill has been used by spies for years. The perforated grill has proved more useful to modern armies, since the concealment is of no special advantage to them and their messages must be of a type suitable for radio or telegraphic transmission.

Concealment always has been important in military correspondence. Late in July, 1777, General John Burgoyne found his army cut off from other British forces by the American rebels in the Hudson River Valley. In an urgent letter, he asked Sir Henry Clinton in New York to send reinforcements. The troops that Burgoyne needed were in Maryland, and Clin-

FIG. 4. *Non-perforated grill*

ton sent him the bad news in a rambling and apparently mean-ingless letter, so phrased as to give away as little as possible to the Colonial troops. Burgoyne's dumbell-shaped grill re-vealed the calamity; forced to fight as best he could with the troops at hand, he lost the great Battle of Saratoga.

Another kind of cipher is produced from a crossbreeding of the grill with the route transposition described in the pre-vious chapter. It is called a "non-perforated grill" (See FIG. 4)*, and it looks something like a crossword puzzle that has not yet been filled in. Both the sender and the receiver must

*In the non-perforated grill in Figure 4, sixteen squares are blacked out to form a regular pattern. In most grills of this type, the squares are blacked out at random.

possess the crossword sheets, with exactly the same squares blacked out. The sender writes his message, AS SOON AS THE GENERAL ARRIVES AT THE BATTLE LINE SHOOT HIM, into the empty spaces of his sheet horizontally from left to right. He then copies it off by a prearranged route, starting, for instance, in the upper left corner, moving down each column, and placing the letters in groups of five. The message he sends is OESLA NNLAA ITAAT NHSSE RTTET RRHTS ISHIE HOEAV BLOMG EEOOR. The last two letters are nulls, inserted to fill out the last five-letter group.

The receiver writes the message into his "crossword puzzle" vertically, with the message beginning at the upper left-hand corner, and gets Figure 4 again. He then reads off the message horizontally. This type of cipher is very hard to break, especially if the message is long enough to prevent the anagramming of likely words. If the operation is performed twice on a long message, it becomes *extremely* difficult to break.

In a simple transposition, a few clues may be enough to give away the shape and size of the diagram. A Q appearing eight letters before a U, for instance, suggests eight as one dimension. The relative location of the parts of other and more common letter pairs may then confirm the assumed value. In a message enciphered with a non-perforated grill, the length of the rows and columns varies. Nevertheless, a skillful cryptanalyst may be able to piece together enough words and word fragments to detect the shape. When the enciphering process is repeated and the message is long, the length of the intervals presents a second irregularity imposed upon the first. Only by groping in the dark for the half-way stage can the cryptanalyst detect the shape of the original diagram.

The *scytale* has many cousins and descendants in the transposition family. Such ciphers are favorites among spies and terrorists, as the key word, route, or pattern is easily memorized, and correspondents need carry no incriminating documents or paraphernalia that would identify them as spies. The more secure transposition ciphers, such as those produced by rotating and non-perforated grills, have proved more useful, by and large, to armies and to diplomats, who can keep their secret work sheets in safe places. Of course, a spy caught with any type of grill or other cipher mechanism on his person would be shot as quickly as his carelessness deserved.

5. Simple Substitutions

A STORY is told about a mental patient in St. Elizabeth's Hospital, in the District of Columbia, who baffled her psychiatrists. At times she seemed to withdraw herself so completely from her surroundings, that she heard and saw nothing. At other times, she would seize pencil and paper and begin to write or draw with furious concentration. The pictures showed charging and rearing horses. The writing, which flowed from her pencil as fast as if she were writing plain English, appeared to be sheer nonsense. She went about it so purposefully, however, that one of the doctors decided it must mean something. He consulted a cipher expert, who recognized it at once as a Julius Caesar cipher. The cryptanalyst was able to read her strange messages and so contributed to her treatment.

In her mind, the horses proved to be symbolic of destructive power and were intimately associated with her long-dead father. He had been an avid horseman, while her invalid mother shrank from animals of all kinds. At the age of three, the patient saw her father thrown and trampled to death. Although her mother had done everything she could to efface not only this terrible memory, but also any recollection of the girl's father, the patient was still, in her subconscious mind, devoted to him.

In her early teens, when she had "forgotten" the sight of her father's death, she kept a diary. Knowing that her mother would pry into anything she did, the girl used secret writing in her private journal. The cipher was so simple that if her mother had had the slightest knowledge of cryptography, she could have read it easily, but apparently she did not. With practice, the girl learned to write almost as quickly in this simple cipher as she could in plain English.

Years later, after her mother, too, had died, the young woman became engaged. Her fiancé, a young man who enjoyed fox hunting, suggested that she take riding lessons. At first the girl refused, but he insisted. At last, she agreed. As she attempted to mount for the first time, her nervousness seemed to communicate itself to the horse. It reared. Her fiancé grabbed the bridle and succeeded in calming the animal, though not without some injury to himself. The girl collapsed completely. She believed that she had killed the man she loved, and that any man close to her was doomed to be struck down by a horse.

Some of this story emerged through the cipher messages, in which she reverted to the style of her diary, long since destroyed by her jealous mother. The rest was reconstructed by the psychiatrists from what she had related to them under the influence of drugs. With her curious past revealed to her, she was at last able to face reality.

What was the nature of the cipher in which the patient wrote? In all the transposition ciphers, whether they are produced by *scytale,* route and column shift, or by grill, the letters keep their own identities. A is always A. The ciphering process changes only their relationship with each other. In "substitution" ciphers, the letters assume arbitarily-chosen equivalents

43

while remaining in the same order. "A" might be written as "B" or as "G", or even a non-literal symbol other than a letter of the alphabet.

This is undoubtedly the most widely-used form of secret writing, and it is over two thousand years old.

The simplest kind of substitution, the sort that the sick woman used, bears a famous name, that of Julius Caesar. Though it was invented long before Caesar, his name has become associated with the replacement of one letter by another, usually the letter three places removed from it in the normal alphabetic sequence. Thus, if the interval is plus three, D is the cipher equivalent of A, E represents B, and C appears for Z. In the Julius Caesar cipher, I LOVE YOU becomes L ORYH BRX. With a little practice, it is almost as easy to write great Caesar's cipher as it is to write in plain language.

There is no reason why a simple substitution should involve anything so obvious as a three-letter shift. It is easy enough to assign some other letter, at random, as the cipher equivalent of any letter. It is possible to use numbers in place of letters Here the simplest cipher may be worked out by using 1 or 01 for A, 2 or 02 for B, 26 for Z, and so forth. Other symbols may be used to represent letters, as # for A, $ for B and the like.

One disadvantage of such substitution alphabets is that it is necessary for anyone using one to carry a key sheet on his person. A spy cannot easily remember cipher equivalents for twenty-six letters. If he is captured with such a key sheet in his pocket, he can hardly deny that he is a spy. He usually is shot at sunrise. One of the first cipher requirements of a spy is that he does not have to carry any memory props with him. He remembers only the system, which does the memorizing for him. Another disadvantage is that any simple substitution is no more secure than plain language.

ROSICRUCIAN CIPHER

A B C	D E F	G H I
J K L	M N O	P Q R
S T U	V W X	Y Z

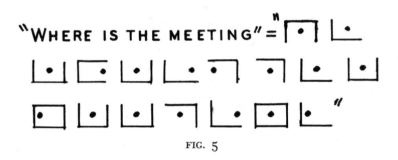

FIG. 5

The Rosicrucian cipher (See FIG. 5) has the advantage of being its own memory device. It requires no written key. The system can be mastered with one quick look, yet a typical message looks baffling until the secret is known.

In the Rosicrucian diagram there are nine spaces, each enclosed with a different combination of lines, and each containing three letters, except for the final space, which holds two. The cipher equivalent of a letter is expressed by indicating the shape of its box and its position relative to the other letters in the box. To encipher the letter W, the sender reproduces the three lines of the box ⊓. Since W is the middle

45

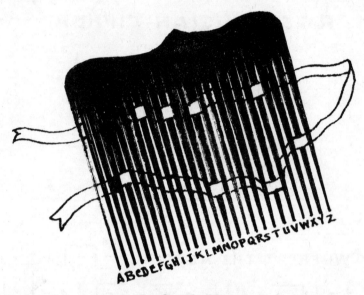

FIG. 6. *Comb-and-ribbon cipher*

letter found in it, he then places a dot in its center: ⊓ . In the same box, the first letter is V. Hence, V is enciphered with the same lines as W, but the dot, instead of being in the middle, is placed in V's position, at the left: ⊓ . It is said that a famous secret society of philosophers, the Rosicrucians (Society of the Rosy Cross), used this cipher to keep its mysteries from public knowledge. This cipher is also known, less elegantly, as the "pigpen," and it has been used by generations of schoolboys and prisoners of war. Because it is a simple substitution that employs symbols instead of letters, it has no security.

Almost anything that provides twenty-six or more alternatives can serve as the basis for a simple substitution. In the days when parents kept strict watch over their daughters and married them off to suit family convenience, a young footman was able to let his lord's daughter know that he loved her. He could twist a ribbon through the teeth of the comb that she had dropped. (See FIG. 6.) Can you read it?

Unlike the Julius Caesar and Rosicrucian ciphers, the comb-and-ribbon cipher does not look like writing. Unless one knows that a secret message is involved, he will miss it entirely and not try to solve it. (More about concealment ciphers appears in Chapters 23, 24, and 28.)

In World War I, a spy organization that helped the Allied cause in German-occupied Belgium based a simple substitution cipher on the first twenty-six words (not counting repetitions) of the "Lord's Prayer." It was cumbersome because a whole word was needed to express a single letter, but there was no risk of having to write down a cipher alphabet or a key word that might betray a man to his enemy.

A simple substitution may resemble just about anything. The zigzag cipher (See FIG. 7) is nothing more than lines connecting points—but the points correspond to letters on a key strip. (See FIG. 8.) The Zigzag has long been a favorite among criminals and students. Like the comb cipher, it disguises its existence. The resemblance of a zigzag cipher to a graph conceals its true identity.

Because they know that ciphers can be disguised so easily, some people see secret messages everywhere, whether or not one really exists. During World War I, an intelligence officer brought a dead carrier pigeon to Herbert Yardley. This was not so strange as it sounds, because Colonel Yardley was the chief of America's new codes and ciphers department, the "Black Chamber." There were small holes in some of the pigeon's wing feathers. Could they be a hidden cipher? Certainly this suggested the zigzag type, and spies were known to be using carrier pigeons. Although he was wrapped up in many other problems, Yardley deposited some of the feathers

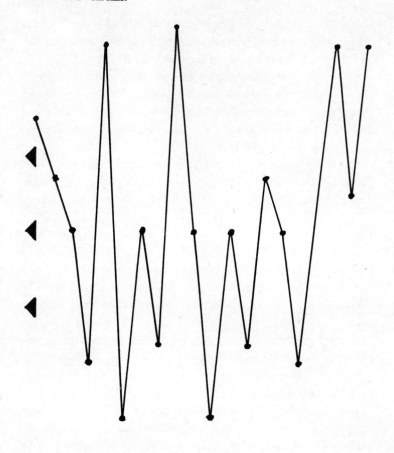

FIG. 7. *Zigzag cipher*

in his desk drawer. When next he examined them, he found more tiny holes. The pigeon was no spy, but it most certainly had lice! It is easy, indeed, for some people to "detect" a cryptogram where none really exists.

FIG. 8. *Zigzag cipher key*

6. Open Code Messages

Shortly after the United States declared war against Germany in 1917, an American family of three left New York for China. Dr. Stifler had accepted a position with the newly-founded Peking Union Medical College. Accompanying him were his wife and little son. Knowing that it might be impossible to obtain any kind of milk for the baby once they were in China, the parents took enough powdered skim milk with them for the long voyage across the Pacific and for a few weeks to follow. Before leaving New York, they made arrangements with Mrs. Stifler's brother to ship further supplies that might be needed. The request was to be sent by cable, as a letter in those days took a month to travel from China to the eastern United States.

On their arrival in Peking, they found that milk in any form was, indeed, unobtainable. Therefore Dr. Stifler sent the pre-arranged cablegram to his brother-in-law. Since transoceanic cables must be paid for by the word, instead of by ten-word units, such as are used in telegrams, the message was as short as possible: MILK, with the signature, STIFLER.

The cablegram was not delivered immediately to Mrs.

Stifler's brother. Instead, he received a call from federal agents, who demanded, "Explain your dealings with Stifler of Peking!" The cable censors had been on their job. A single cryptic word, followed by a German name, had aroused their suspicions. Fortunately, the brother was able to satisfy them concerning the innocence of the message, and the baby received his milk on schedule.

Not all such communications are so harmless. The sending of "open code" messages, which sounded like humdrum family or business telegrams, but which were really prearranged spy signals, flourished in both World Wars. A man in England, suspected of working for the Germans in World War I, filed at the telegraphic office a message that stated simply, "Father is dead." Before transmitting this piece of family news to the addressee in neutral Holland, an alert censor altered the text to read, "Father is deceased," and sat back to await developments. An anguished reply sped back from the Netherlands: "Is Father *deceased* or *dead?*" This was enough evidence for the British authorities, and the German agent in Holland received no further word from his spying "relative," who presumably died very quickly of bad secret writing.

Wartime restrictions on telegrams often were flouted in ingenious ways. Traffic was so heavy, that individuals were forbidden to send messages of greeting or congratulation. An American Air Force officer stationed in England was deeply disappointed when informed that he could not congratulate his closest friend, whose wedding was about to take place in New York. He thought the matter over and then filed this cablegram: "Fully approve lifetime partnership you are now contracting." The text was accepted and duly transmitted as a business message.

Open codes were so seriously regarded in America during World War II, that radio stations were forbidden to play records requested by their listeners. It would have been altogether too easy for a lurking enemy sub to surface some fine evening and wait to hear whether "Sally" had requested her local station to play "Stardust" for her birthday—meaning, perhaps, that a convoy would sail at midnight.

In 1939, a naturalized American citizen was deeply distressed to receive a letter from his father, who still lived in Germany. The letter had passed through Nazi censorship easily. Previous letters had been noncommittal, but this one was a glowing account of life in Hitler's Reich. Why should the son have felt concern? All the earlier letters had been written in English. Father and son had agreed in whispers behind closed doors, during the younger man's last visit to Berlin, that any letters the father wrote in English were to be accepted as the truth. Any letter in German, however, was to be taken as the opposite of its open meaning. The last letter was in German.

A refinement of this technique was invented by an Armenian family which had settled in Lebanon after the Revolution had driven them from their home in Russia. The Communists used every sort of blandishment to induce young men who were valuable as laborers to return. At last, three brothers were talked into going back to Russia. They knew the Communists would pressure them into sending for their families. Before leaving Turkey, they agreed with their relatives that in their first letter they would send a snapshot of themselves. If the picture showed the group standing up, it would mean that all was well, and that the family should start packing. But if the picture showed them sitting down, the family was to understand that the worker's paradise was not as advertised, and that it would be safer to stay put.

At last the letter arrived, full of praise for the life in Communist Armenia. Enclosed was the promised picture of the three young men—lying flat on the ground.

In 1942, an American soldier, about to be sent overseas, arranged a method for letting his family know his destination without arousing the suspicions of the military censors. He told them that he would use a different middle initial for his father's name in the address of each successive letter. Together, the letters would spell out his post of duty.

The soldier was sent to North Africa as part of Eisenhower's army in Tunis. He spelled out the name of the region in his next five letters home. It did not occur to him to number his letters, and he had always been careless about dates. Neither the soldier nor his parents had anticipated the order in which the letters found their way to the little Indiana town he called home. The mail service provided the unsuspecting family with an anagram of their son's location. His mother and father consulted all the atlases in the public library and studied his little sister's geography book, but they never found NUTSI.

Letters have the virtue of a personal touch; there is an impersonal quality to telegraphic and radio messages. Yet a manual radio or telegraphic sending technique can be identified. Each telegrapher uses a characteristic pressure pattern on the sending key, and this can reveal his identity to a knowledgeable receiver.

During the Civil War, an enterprising Union officer of the recently-organized Army Signal Corps succeeded in cutting into a Confederate wire south of Washington. The opportunity was too good to miss. He proceeded to tap out messages to the Confederate units he had identified by listening in. His false orders were intended to lead them into a Union trap, but the Southerners were not fooled for a minute. They recognized the change in transmitting technique and promptly tapped back, "We know you're there—get off our wire, you Damyankee."

Today, machines send out the signals from automatic transmitters, and the personal touch is usually missing. Only in the work of amateurs, or in furtive messages of spies, tapping on hidden transmitters, can the hand of an individual sender still be recognized.

In World War II, the British dropped a spy over the Netherlands to help organize the Dutch underground for resistance to the Nazis, and to send vital information to England. He carried with him a short-wave radio transmitter. Soon British intelligence began to receive a steady stream of messages sent in the prearranged cipher and on the assigned wave length, tapped out unmistakably by the agent himself.

Acting on this news, the Royal Air Force repeatedly bombed the area designated as important targets, Nazi airfields, and supply dumps. On raid after raid, the planes were greeted with heavy anti-aircraft fire, and Nazi military strength seemed greater than ever. More agents were parachuted into Holland, as the spy directed, and word, still sent by the first spy's hand, announced their safe arrival.

In time, the British began to suspect that all was not well. After the war, the whole story came out. The original spy had been captured almost before his parachute touched the ground. The Nazis, using their usual brutal methods of torture and threats against the man's relatives, had forced him to deceive his allies. In desperation, he tried to warn them by using an extra letter in his cipher. Through a mixup, no one had understood the danger signal. The "airfields" and "supply dumps" had been open fields, sometimes equipped with dummy installations, and always ringed with anti-aircraft guns. The later agents had been seized and killed as fast as they had landed.

On another occasion, the Royal Air Force had better luck. The Nazis built a simulated airfield, with flimsy mocked-up wooden buildings and planes. A single British plane flew over and dropped one small bomb—made of wood.

British intelligence also helped to insure the tactical surprise needed for the Normandy invasion. Shortly before the scheduled landings, newspapers carried a story about the loss at sea of a plane bound from England to North Africa. A little later, the body of a British staff officer was washed ashore near a little fishing village on the northern coast of Spain. The British embassy rushed a representative to the spot to claim the body and all papers contained in the personal effects of the deceased. However, the Nazis bribed the Spanish authorities. Before the body was surrendered to the proper claimants, it was thoroughly searched, and all documents were photographed. There were indiscreet letters and official orders, indicating that the United States and Britain had postponed the invasion of France in order to launch assaults against islands in the Mediterranean.

The whole affair was a colossal hoax. British intelligence had carefully manufactured an imaginary identity for this dead "staff officer" by planting stories in newspapers and mentioning him in official communiques. Actually, a civilian, who had died of natural causes, served his country after death more spectacularly than many heroes of the battlefield. Only a careful autopsy could have revealed that it was pneumonia, not drowning, that had taken his life. With the bereaved family's consent, the corpse had been dressed in a uniform the man had never worn in life and the pockets had been stuffed with artfully-contrived documents. The officer who had never existed was then dropped, with full honors, from a submarine, into the current that bore him to the Spanish coast. Nazi curiosity and bribery did the rest. Members of the German High Command were so thoroughly convinced of the authenticity of this information, that they acted upon it, with fatal consequences.

7. When Words Change
Their Names

THERE is an old game called "Teakettle." The person who is "It" goes out of the room, and the other players agree on a certain word. When "It" returns, the others start asking questions. In each question, "teakettle" is used in place of the chosen word. If "fair" (fare) is selected, the questions might be, "Do you think the gym teacher is teakettle?" or "Did he try to get out of paying his teakettle on the bus?" "It" tries to identify the word from a minimum of questions.

In the games of crime, war, and international intrigue, "Teakettle" is played in deadly earnest. For centuries, plotters have preferred to use a harmless-sounding word in place of a proper name that might give them away. In the seventeenth century, for instance, French diplomats referred to the Pope as "the rose" and to Rome as "the garden."

In World War II, pilots addressed each other on voice radio with such prearranged names as "Popeye" and "Mickey Mouse." Names were invented for reference to military operations, such as TORCH for the invasion of North Africa, OVERLORD for the liberation of France, and FORAGER for the assault on the Marianas. MANHATTAN PROJECT meant the atomic bomb. One OSS agent who had it in for his superior registered his code name as GENERAL COLBY IS A BAS-TARD (name fictitious).

The choice of code names is terribly important. The word should be easily remembered, readily distinguished from other words, and totally unrelated to its true meaning.

Oddly enough, in choosing a code word, one may give away the whole show. In World War II, one branch of the Office of Strategic Services designated the surveillance of King Farouk of Egypt by the word WOMEN. This was much too obvious a choice for anyone who knew how that monarch amused himself.

The code word ABRAHAM was chosen for the "Octagon" conference of Roosevelt and Churchill, which opened on September 11, 1944. Quebec, the location of the meeting, was top secret. One young officer, who remembered his history, embarrassed his superiors by guessing the meeting place at once. He consciously recalled (as the inventor of the name had perhaps unconsciously remembered) that the decisive engagement in the Siege of Quebec in 1759 had been fought on the Plains of Abraham.

In peace as well as in war, people play at this "Teakettle" game. In 1960, the announcement of the engagement of King Baudouin of the Belgians to Doña Fabiola of Spain astonished the high society of Europe. How had a ruling monarch been able to go courting without a legion of newspapermen at his heels? The answer proved to be that the young couple had done most of their dating by long-distance international telephone, using a private code. An exhibition of parachute jumping had been in progress when they met, briefly, for the first time. From then on, partly because of some confusion among her own servants, Doña Fabiola's household referred to the young man who kept calling up as "the parachutist."

The King of the Belgians and his future Queen were actually following precedent in using their royal code. The use of ciphers and codes, insofar as they existed, was regarded as the exclusive rights of kings and their agents until the seventeenth century. When the Earl of Somerset was tried for treason, Sir Francis Bacon introduced into the proceedings the fact that the Earl had communicated with his associates in cipher. Although Bacon himself was a cryptographer with original ideas he called cipher "a process reserved for Kings and Princes in their affairs of state."

It is hard to believe that such a prohibition ever could have been strictly enforced. Thousands of people would be liable for trial on treason charges today if such were the law. Many families have private words to cover everything from bathroom to birthday party. Snooping teachers and supervisors often earn for themselves such code names as "Pussyfoot." As in the "Teakettle" game, the context gives the game away.

If an alias is used for every word in a message, the message is said to be in code. Most people regard a page of jumbled words, letters, or numbers as a code. Actually, all secret writing may be called "cipher," though the term is usually applied to transpositions and substitutions involving single letters or pairs of letters, but "code" means a special type of substitution. Every group of letters or numbers stands for a syllable, word, phrase, or even a whole sentence.

ATTACK AT DAWN may be enciphered in many ways. If it is to be *encoded,* there must be a book giving equivalents for each word or phrase. The code clerk looks under A to find ATTACK and AT, and under D for DAWN, much as he would look for meanings in a dictionary. The plain text expressions must be listed alphabetically in the book. Sometimes, the code words are also in order. If this is the case, the code is said to be "one-part." The book might read as follows:

a	ABABA
. . .	. . .
at	AQORE
. . .	. . .
attack	AREBA
. . .	. . .
dawn	CUVAB
. . .	. . .

The coded message would then be AREBA AQORE CUVAB.

Dictionaries have been used as code books. The page number (three figures) followed by the number of a word on the page (two figures) make up a five-digit symbol for the word.

Shortly after America become involved in World War I, German agents in Mexico began communicating with Berlin in a new code. It takes months to compile, print, and distribute code books. American cryptographers reasoned correctly that no such book had been smuggled into Mexico through the Allied blockade. They guessed that the Germans were actually using a dictionary, and they started a search for it. They were so successful that eventually an officer strolled into the Library of Congress and pulled a copy of the right dictionary off the shelf. That dictionary made history by unlocking Germany's military secrets, and many Germans died of "bad secret writing."

A much safer code book may be drawn up by using two sections. Just as a foreign language dictionary can be divided into two parts—French-English and English-French—with each section in alphabetical order, so a "two-part" code has its plain-to-code and code-to-plain divisions. In a two-part code, the message ATTACK AT DAWN might be ONIZA BULAX FOVEP:

Encoding:		*Decoding:*	
a	. MOGIT	BULAX	at
. . .	. . .	. . .	. . .
at	BULAX	FOVEP	dawn
. . .	. . .	. . .	. . .
attack	ONIZA	MOGIT	a
. . .	. . .	. . .	. . .
dawn	FOVEP	ONIZA	attack
. . .	. . .	. . .	. . .

There is much more security in a two-part code, though the book is twice as thick.

When the German agents in Mexico turned in desperation to the use of a dictionary in 1917, they did so for a good reason. The German foreign service had been equipped with excellent, carefully-compiled codes. Messages broadcast in this system were intercepted by the Allies, though they might never have succeeded in breaking the code but for the help of a cryptographic clerk stationed in Brussels. The young man, Alexander Szek, was the son of an Austrian father and an English mother. His sympathies lay with the British. Whenever he was alone with the code book, he memorized or jotted down key groups with their meanings. Over a period of months, he smuggled his gleanings to an English agent, who, in turn, succeeded in getting the material to London.

At last, the British could read top-secret German diplomatic correspondence. When the Germans plotted with Mexico to embroil the United States in war with Japan early in 1917, the

British were able to decode the whole story, word for word. Since England was determined to bring America into the war, even if it meant letting the Germans know that they could read the code, His Majesty's Government revealed the text of the famous Zimmermann note.

The American people were horrified to realize that the Kaiser's agents had actually promised to turn over our southwestern states to Mexico in return for this piece of treachery. America's declaration of war was not long in following. (The Zimmermann affair is covered in detail in Chapter 9.)

The British tried to conceal the source of the code-book leak. One of their spokesmen, Admiral Hall, asked reporters, "Wasn't it clever of the Americans to do just what we have been trying to do ever since the war started? They succeeded in stealing the original text of a German diplomatic telegram." The Germans were either not fooled, or they suspected Szek for other reasons. Their agents apparently murdered him before the British could smuggle him to safety, and the German diplomats were hastily instructed in the use of different code systems.

The extensive use of carefully prepared codes goes back to the development of telegraphic and radio communication. The alteration of a single letter may change the meaning of a whole plain—or cipher—word. Consider the likeness in appearance of such utterly different words as "united" and "untied", or "nuclear" and "unclear." "Unclear blast observed in Pacific" casts doubt on the location of an explosion, while "Nuclear blast observed . . ." might indicate anything from a new series of tests to the outbreak of war.

Telegrams and radiograms are often garbled. By preparing two-part code books on scientific principles, cryptographers almost eliminate the possibility that error will alter a meaning. Also, a message itself can be so shortened, or condensed, by the use of a good code, that it is actually cheaper to send than a plain language telegram.

For these reasons, commercial codes are used widely in business. The code books may be found in cable offices and in libraries, and anyone who wants to send a safe message at low cost usually may use them.

An American secretary once sent a commercial code message to her boss in China without including the name of the code. The boss spent nearly an hour thumbing through the available books before he found that the message made sense in Bentley's Second Phrase Code.

In 1925, Miss Bertha Blount, an American teacher in Thailand, returned on furlough to the United States. As the principal of a Presbyterian school, she was known to most of the American missionaries in Bangkok, and was especially dear to George B. McFarland, MD, DDS. This unusual man worked tirelessly to serve God and his fellow men in Thailand as practicing physician and teacher of medicine, as personal dentist to King Rama VI (uncle of the present King and grandson of King Mongkut, who engaged Anna Leonowens to be his children's governess), as president of the company that produced the first usable Thai typewriter, and as compiler of the encyclopedic dictionary that bears his name. For all this, and more, the King bestowed a title of nobility on him.

A medical emergency kept the busy Dr. McFarland from seeing Miss Blount in private before she sailed back to the States. He wanted to tell her that he loved her and that he hoped to marry her. If they were to be married, however, the mission board would have to be informed as soon as possible. An exchange of letters would be much too slow. A cable would be fast, but not at all private; cable clerks could not be trusted to keep their mouths shut about so well-known a man. The couple would not enjoy airing their romance in public.

Dr. McFarland's brilliant and versatile mind came up with

the answer—commercial code. Just which code and what words he used remain the McFarlands' secret. Commercial codes are not designed for romantic correspondence, but it is a safe guess that he might have expressed "deep consideration" and urged her to "consider a merger." It was easier for her to cable back—something like "Yes, agreed."

They were married on her return to Thailand, and remained there until after the outbreak of World War II. Even the invading Japanese, who commandeered American houses and interned their owners, did not dare to dislodge the McFarlands from their home. The doctor died in 1942. His widow eventually reached the USA with the American diplomatic staff on the *Gripsholm*.

When the United States Government asked Thai nationals residing in this country what Allied name meant most to their people, they chose no soldier, diplomat, or governess, but Dr. George B. McFarland. Thus it was that, in 1944, a liberty ship was launched bearing his name. The Kaiser shipyard officials asked Mrs. McFarland to christen the ship, but they did so with some hesitation because the launching was scheduled for 4:00 A.M.—an unseemly hour for a lady to visit the waterfront. Mrs. McFarland, however, graciously accepted their invitation. She did not bother to tell them, as she later confided with a chuckle to one of the authors of this book, that she habitually worked the "graveyard" shift, midnight until 8:00 A.M., at the Office of War Information, from which she was granted a night off in honor of the occasion. The lady who had received and accepted a marriage proposal in commercial code could take all sorts of things in her stride.

Quite a different matter from legitimate commercial code is the use by business of code designations for purposes of secrecy. In 1961, during the investigation of price-fixing by electric companies fulfilling government contracts, it was revealed that the guilty officials used a private code to discuss their deals: "1" meant General Electric, "2" stood for West-inghouse, "3" denoted Allis-Chalmers, and so forth. Several men who ranked high in their companies were sent to jail for the illegal rigging of contracts. Partly due to the code, other company officials had been completely unaware of the conspiracy.

Some code groups seem to develop a life of their own. Since they are pronounceable, they stick in the ear of a cryptographic clerk. To an imaginative person, the artificial words develop a personality of their own. The late humorist James Thurber was a code clerk in the American mission in Paris after World War I, which service to his country may well have contributed to his gradual loss of sight. Years later, when he came to write his delightful fable, *The Thirteen Clocks,* Thurber turned to the old code groups he had dealt with in naming such characters as the effervescent Golux and the loathsome Todal.

Unlike code, cipher messages rarely present pronounceable groups. A cipher can be devised that uses consonants and vowels in pairs, to achieve the effect of a code, but any good cryptanalyst can tell at once that it is not a code.

The following conversation was once reported as having been overheard at a Brooklyn lunch counter:

FUNEX?   SVFX.

FUNEM?   SVFM.

FUMNX?   SVFMNX.

OKMNX!

Is this code or cipher? Neither, of course. It is a phonetic equivalent of "Have you any eggs? . . . Okay, ham and eggs!"

8. Code Books

Why has not code completely supplanted cipher?

In the Russo-Turkish War in 1877, a code book led to the destruction of the Turkish army. Osman Pasha telegraphed Constantinople from his fortress at Plevna on the Danube for instructions. Should he move out his army of forty thousand to join the main body of the Turkish forces, or should he sortie to attack a Russian column that was crossing the Danube?

Headquarters replied in a brand-new code, which German experts had just prepared for the Turkish army. Osman Pasha's communications officer, Selim Pasha, was out on a tour of inspection, and, true to his security instructions, he was carrying the only copy of the code book on his own person. A Russian patrol prevented Selim's return, and before Osman Pasha ever learned the contents of his telegram, Plevna was cut off. Despite a heroic defense, it was captured eventually by the Russians.

On March 12, 1884, a huge uprising of the Sudanese tribes

under the inspired leadership of the Mahdi had surrounded the city of Khartoum, where the British General Charles George ("Chinese") Gordon held out with a handful of loyal troops. The Mahdi was content to wait. Day by day, the waters of the Nile were falling, and he knew that soon his savage tribesmen could seize the city.

Gordon was equally aware of his plight. On September 10, its last voyage for that season, the river boat *Abbas* sailed north from the beleaguered city, carrying Gordon's second-in-command, to whom he had entrusted all his cryptographic materials. They had to be kept out of the Mahdi's hands even if Khartoum fell.

From that day on, secret communications between Khartoum and the outside world were impossible. When Gordon's friends succeeding in sending messages to him, he could not read them because of the loss of his cryptographic equipment. He hardly dared reply in plain language. The *Abbas* never reached Cairo. It ran aground and was seized by the Mahdi's men who gloatingly announced its capture on October 22.

On January 26, 1885, just before the expedition to relieve Khartoum arrived, the city fell, and Gordon was slain on the steps of his Governor's Palace. Some sort of cipher that could have been committed to memory might have saved the army and a quarter of a million square miles.

It is a general practice to change codes or ciphers at pre-arranged times. Great care must be taken to provide that all correspondents begin to use the new system at the same moment, because a duplicate message sent in both ciphers would jeopardize the new one. Cipher keys can be switched with relative ease, but it is no simple task to distribute new code books.

In 1944, a member of the Office of Strategic Services killed a German agent in Barcelona and started communicating with the Germans in the code he had captured. The German spy's radio messages to Berlin on Allied ship movements had been of enormous value to German wolf-pack submarines until the American agent horned in on his act.

For weeks, the OSS man sent the German U-boats on wild-goose chases all over the North Atlantic. One day, the American agent received from Germany, on his wave length, and at his assigned time, a message that was pure gibberish. He realized that code-changing time had arrived. Lamely, he sent back a message asking the Germans please to continue to use the old system, as he had not yet received the new book. All he received from the Germans was silence.

It is a long and tedious operation to draw up a code book. Once such a top-secret document is distributed, the utmost care must be taken to prevent its falling into enemy hands. An army in the field, or a spy in a hostile country, often finds the use of code not worth the risks involved.

The situation of a ship at sea is very different from that of an army on land. Messages from ships in battle are usually full of numbers—degrees of latitude and longtitude, courses, speeds, bearings, and ranges. To be enciphered, numbers must be written out, and the task is at best cumbersome. Code words express figures more safely and accurately.

In the message ENEMY SIGHTED COURSE TWO SEVEN FIVE BEARING ONE FOUR ZERO SPEED TWENTY FIVE KNOTS, sixty-eight letters (fourteen groups) must be laboriously enciphered. A well-planned naval code could express the same text in six to nine code groups, with considerably less strain on a communications officer, who might well be trying to concentrate while his ship rolls and pitches, or even shudders under shellfire.

Nor is the code book itself in much danger on a ship. Capture at sea is not unknown in modern warfare, but it is a rarity. Whether an unlucky ship is blown to bits, set afire, or damaged so badly that it is sure to sink, its code book is relatively safe from enemy eyes. This was not always so. After the British battleship HMS *Victoria* sank in 1893, one of the few things found floating on the surface was a box containing the most precious and secret object on the ship, Her Britannic Majesty's naval code book. Since then, to make certain that the precious book goes down with its ship, navy codes have been bound in heavy lead covers.

The lead was not always sufficient to safeguard naval secrets. Early in World War I, the German cruiser *Magdeburg* ran aground on the Baltic coast. The Russians recovered her code books, and for nearly two years the British were able to decrypt the orders every German ship received at sea.

It was thus that they were able to intercept and destroy a German squadron at Dogger Bank on January 24, 1915. At the great battle of Jutland, on May 16, 1916, the British missed an opportunity to destroy the German High Seas Fleet. The air was so jam-packed with messages, that the cryptographers could not get through to Admiral Jellicoe. By using faked recognition signals and by employing excellent naval tactics, the Germans twice extricated themselves from seemingly hopeless positions.

Jutland convinced the German Navy that it was time for a thoroughgoing change of codes. The new codes they developed kept Germany's secrets until a U-boat was sunk near the British coast in shallow water. (See Chapter 9.) An English diver recovered the code book, and the game was on again. The Allies could understand what the submarines were saying to each other on their wireless, but they still could not identify the U-boats because their designations had been changed, nor could they determine their locations, which were keyed to a special map.

The German Navy had airships as well as surface vessels and submarines. In October, 1917, a crippled Zeppelin, out of fuel and battered by a gale, dropped to earth in northern France. The nearest town was Chaumont, which happened to be American Army Headquarters. An American intelligence officer, reasoning rightly that the code books could not have been sunk over land or burned in a hydrogen-filled airship, guessed that they might have been torn to bits and thrown overboard as the Zeppelin came to ground. His men searched the vast area over which it had traveled, and returned with twenty-two sacks of paper scraps. Then began the tremendous puzzle of fitting together the bits. Some of the pieces were blue and showed parts of the coastline. Pieced together, they proved to be the key map, with co-ordinates showing the stations of German submarines all over the world.

A little book, which one of the men had picked up as a souvenir, provided pictures of German naval vessels of all types, with their coded identifications. More defeat by secret writing came in the months that followed.

In June of 1944, in World War II, an American submarine-hunting task group, with the escort carrier *Guadalcanal* as its flagship, attacked a German U-boat. Its captain, believing his ship to be irreparably damaged, gave orders to abandon ship and to open the valves that would scuttle it. However, a specially-trained handful of Americans succeeded in boarding the sinking sub and capturing it almost intact.

This feat, unparalleled since the War of 1812, remained a well-guarded secret until the war was over. It can scarcely have failed to affect our knowledge of German communications. There is no better, and, certainly, no faster way of breaking an enemy's codes than by actually getting hold of his books.

While any country at war may profit from knowing the naval and military operations of its enemies, any country at peace or at war may profit from reading the secret diplomatic correspondence of other nations. An embassy has this in common with a ship—its contents are usually safe from seizure. For this reason, most diplomatic correspondence for the past seventy-five years has been carried on in code rather than cipher. Simple code is not secure enough to safeguard the top-secret negotiations of diplomats. Their messages often are written first in code (encoded), and then the coded text is translated into cipher (reciphered or superenciphered). The more elaborate cipher systems described in subsequent chapters give some hint of the problems such messages present to any would-be eavesdroppers.

The Turkish defeat at Plevna showed the world that it is not practical or safe for the average individual to carry a large code book on his person. This is especially true when its very existence might be enough to land its owner in a jail cell or in front of a firing squad.

Criminals and spies usually use cipher for written messages. Some efforts have been made to invent memory codes, but few minds are capable of using them.

By and large, codes have proved useful to diplomats and to naval officers. Today, they have been largely superseded by cipher machines. Like a code book, a cipher machine is best kept in a relatively safe place with a handy source of power—on a ship or in an embassy.

9. Admiral Hall and Room 40

MORE than any war in history, World War I was a vast battle of codes and ciphers. The wireless had just been invented, and in those days, it was not directional. Anyone within range and on the right wave length, could pick up any message that was sent out.

The war's enormous distances made it impossible to keep enemy ports and ships under surveillance by frigates and other vessels. The airplane was not yet sufficiently developed for observation purposes. Thus, the ability to crack enemy wireless messages in code or cipher (and often a combination of both) was vital to combat operations.

The Code Warfare really began on August 20, 1914, when the German lighter cruiser *Magdeburg* was attacked and destroyed by Russian warships in the Gulf of Finland. The body of the *Magdeburg's* wireless operator was washed ashore, and to everyone's astonishment, he was still clutching his copy of the German High Seas Fleet Naval Code. The Russians with a co-operation and generosity they certainly did not extend to their Allies in World War II, turned the captured German code book over to the British Navy.

The war's greatest administrative genius in the code-and-cipher-cracking business was British Admiral Sir William Reginald Hall, Director of British Naval Intelligence. Admiral Hall, whose father was the first Director, set his staff to work on the problem of decoding German fleet messages through the precious code book. Their attempts proved fruitless until they discovered that the Germans were using a cipher on top of their naval code to make it ultra safe. One of Admiral Hall's cryptographers finally succeeded in finding the key to the cipher, and, for the next three months, every wireless message between fleet units of the German Navy and Berlin was decrypted by the English.

Whenever the Germans would change the key to the cipher, the British cryptographers would break it. For a time the Germans changed the key once a week, and later they revised it every twenty-four hours.

Admiral Hall greatly increased the number of cryptographers in what he called his "Room 40." Because of the scarcity of top brains, he initiated the radical step of hiring women for this function—the first time in history that women were used as cryptographers. The cryptographers of Room 40 became so proficient, that even when the German ciphers were being changed each day, they usually succeeded in cracking a new cipher by the second eight-hour shift following change.

Admiral Hall soon found that the Germans possessed many different code books that were used exclusively by certain services, and even in certain geographical areas. Inasmuch as it is almost impossible to solve a code without getting one's hands on the book, Hall did everything in his power to capture such rarities. He alerted everyone in all of the British services to keep their eyes open for any hint or clue that might lead to an enemy code book. By a great stroke of luck, in December, 1914, a British fishing trawler brought up a German code book in her nets. Immediately, Hall's staff unraveled a whole new classification of wireless messages from German sources.

Not long after this incident, Admiral Hall learned that the German Vice Consul to Persia had been surprised in the act of trying to destroy the Abadan pipeline, and had fled so precipitately, that he had left his baggage behind. Reasoning that if a diplomatic saboteur wished to communicate with home base, he would want to do so secretly, the Admiral decided that he might have been carrying a code book. Hall immediately instituted a search for the captured baggage, and when it was finally located in the basement of a government building, it was found to contain the extraordinarily valuable German Empire code book for the Middle East. Again, as in the case of the book brought up by the trawler's nets, a whole new spectrum of secret messages ceased to be secrets.

The solution of codes and ciphers is always tedious and sometimes impossible. Analysis is greatly simplified if a code book can be stolen, a work sheet recovered, or a cryptographic clerk bribed. Cryptanalysts have been known to refer to such short cuts as "practical cryptanalysis."

Hall was the war's greatest genius of "practical cryptanalysis."

Whenever a German or Austrian vessel or Zeppelin was sunk, he would attempt to locate the wreck and send down divers to recover the code books.

The extremes to which Room 40 went to obtain a new code book after a change had been made is illustrated by the extraordinary case of the German submarine *UC-44*, which had been laying mines in British harbors.

The British had a special cipher that was used by their own mine sweepers to inform the ships of the Royal Navy of the exact location of those lanes that had been swept clean. It was obvious to Hall that the Germans had cracked this

British mine-sweeping cipher. Shortly after a mine sweeper would issue an "all clear," the German mine-layers would return with their submarines and resow the safe alley with new mines.

Admiral Hall knew that the German U-boat *UC-44* was laying mines off the shallow Port of Waterford, and that it was using a new code book. Therefore, he broadcast a message in the mine-sweeping code that he knew the Germans had cracked, indicating that a safe path had been swept through the middle of the Waterford mine field they had laid down a few days before. The German cryptographers in Berlin picked up the message, deciphered it, and the high command wirelessed the *UC-44* to return with its mines and close up the gap.

Of course, the mines had not been swept, and the *UC-44* hit one and sank in shallow water off Waterford. Admiral Hall immediately sent his divers down to rescue the code book.

From the time the *Magdeburg* sank until the end of 1917, Room 40 was able to keep the British Navy informed of the positions of most of the units of the German High Seas Fleet. The military value of such a feat is beyond calculation, and Admiral Hall must rank with Rossignol as a master cryptographer.

In order to help France, Room 40 provided the French Navy with copies of the captured German code books, and even wirelessed to the French each day in a special cipher regarding the German cipher key of that particular day. This enabled the French to keep track of all German Fleet units operating off their coast.

The subtle mind of Admiral Hall was not content with cracking German codes. He became a past master at planting false British code books on the Germans, and then sending out messages that would lead them into traps.

Once Hall directed one of his agents to allow a German

blonde in a Dutch hotel to steal a fake code book. He soon discovered that even fake books were worth a lot of money. After selling a false code to the Germans for five hundred pounds (almost two thousand dollars), he realized that he had entered a lucrative business. Through his agents, the wily Admiral bargained like mad until the Germans paid through the nose for the false code books he was manufacturing in an annex to Room 40.

Hall was always careful not to jeopardize his phony codes by sending false messages that were not important. Each phony code was elaborately built up with correct facts until the Germans had complete confidence in it. Then, at the worst possible moment, the ax would fall.

The Fleet Admiral of the Royal Navy, Sir David Beatty, would often steam out of a harbor with the fleet in confirmation of one of Admiral Hall's false messages. The largest fleet on earth would maneuver, at the cost of millions of dollars, merely to make a false code book seem real. However, the return on this expensive investment was enormous, and contributed heavily to the Allied victory in World War I.

Admiral Hall's planted codes came in handy in 1916 when the British were facing almost unbearable pressure on the Western Front. The army authorities asked the Admiral if he could dream up some way to relieve the pressure and get part of the German army shifted elsewhere.

Admiral Hall immediately got to work on a "diversion" designed to persuade the Germans that the British were planning an attack from the sea on northern Belgium. He sent messages out, in all the false codes he had planted on the Germans. Of course, the messages were picked up immediately by the Germans, decoded, and assumed to be genuine.

Hall then ordered his agents all over the world to circulate in men's clubs, and other places where rumors could be started, and drop hints about the coming North Belgian front. He had special editions of British newspapers printed, in which articles cleverly suggested a new front; the censors crossed out the paragraphs containing the hints, and then the newspapers were permitted to fall into the hands of known German agents. These fake censored newspapers quickly found their way back to Germany, and further confirmed the "North Belgian invasion."

Admiral Hall's "diversion" succeeded beyond anyone's wildest imagination. As each succeeding false confirmation concerning the new front reached the German General Staff, thousands of soldiers were shifted from the Western Front to guard the Belgian beaches opposite Dover. Strong defenses were set up to repel the expected landing. British fleet units and observers stationed along the Dover shore, immediately observed this concentration of Germans opposite the narrowest part of the English Channel. Everyone jumped to the conclusion that the Germans were planning to invade England, and the English experienced their biggest invasion scare of World War I. Coastal towns were evacuated, troops and territorial guards were brought into the area, and fortifications were thrown up. The British right hand hadn't yet found out what the British left hand was up to.

Every increase in activity on the English side caused the Germans to rush in more troops to stop the English invasion, which, in turn encouraged the English to make more preparations to stop the German invasion. Admiral Hall was in the extraordinarily embarrassing position of not being able to admit he had dreamed up the whole invasion. His great fear was that he might jeopardize the false code books he had so carefully planted on the Germans. Finally, the whole thing was straightened out at top level.

Peculiarly enough, the greatest Naval battle of World War

I, the Battle of Jutland, found the air waves so cluttered with thousands of wireless signals flying in every direction, that the extraordinary cryptographic facilities of Room 40 could not be brought fully into play. The situation was further complicated by the fact that before the battle started, a cryptographic mistake shook the Admirals' confidence in Room 40. Recognizing from their analyses of the battle that their codes had been jeopardized, the Germans revised most of their Naval codes and ciphers.

One amusing incident in the closing stages of the Battle of Jutland highlighted the complexities of the cipher war. The British Fleet, anxious to involve the German High Seas Fleet in a general action, carried on its pursuit under cover of darkness. All this while the extremely jittery British Admiralty had no idea where its ships were located.

The German cryptographers, who must have been unusually able, picked up certain wireless messages between British warships—messages that were not audible in London. They decoded them on the spot, encoded them in their own system, and wirelessed the positions of the British ships to the fleeing units of the German fleet. These coded messages from Germany's most powerful wireless station, the one at Nanen, were, in turn, picked up in England and quickly unscrambled by the cryptographers of Room 40. Finally, after the messages had gone through the hands of two groups of battling cryptographers, the British Admiralty was able to locate its missing fleet.

After the Battle of the Falkland Islands, on December 8, 1914, the victorious British fleet was horrified to find that one German cruiser, the formidable *Dresden,* had somehow escaped in the confusion and was threatening Allied commerce. It was perfectly possible that with a little luck, a swift warship of this type, with its 4.1-inch guns, might actually sink enough

Allied shipping to affect the entire course of the war. The British fleet failed to locate the *Dresden;* the cruiser had mysteriously vanished into the South Atlantic.

Weeks later, a message fell into the hands of the cryptographers of Room 40. It gave the startling news that the elusive *Dresden* was to meet a collier at Juan Fernandez Island off the coast of Chile. The powerful British battle crusier *Kent*, a monster with fourteen 6-inch guns, and the light cruiser *Glasgow*, were immediately sent to lay a trap at the rendezvous. When the *Dresden* arrived, it was sunk, and hundreds of brave Germans went to their death.

Most historians agree that if the United States had not entered World War I, Germany and the Central Powers might have been victorious. Our entry into the war, and the demolition of the U-boat blockade, which was choking England to death, purchased the Allies sufficient breathing time to build up their European forces.

If it can be said that a single man brought the United States into the war against Germany, that man was Admiral Hall. Although Americans were infuriated by the U-boat war, and by Germany's blockade of England, they were determined to keep out of the struggle. The public generally agreed with Wilson's curious statement, "We are too proud to fight."

On January 16, 1917, the German Foreign Minister, Arthur Zimmermann, sent the following cable in the German foreign office cipher to the German Ambassador in Mexico, Dr. Eckhardt:

January 1, 1917

We intend to begin on the first of February unrestricted submarine warfare. We shall endeavour in spite of this to keep the U.S.A. neutral. In the event of this not succeeding we make Mexico a proposal of alliance on the following terms:

Make war together.

Make peace together.

Generous financial support and an undertaking on our part that Mexico is to reconquer the lost territory in Texas, New Mexico and Arizona. The settlement in detail is left to you.

You will inform the President of the above most secretly as soon as the outbreak of war with U.S.A. is certain, and add the suggestion that he should on his own initiative invite Japan to immediate adherence and at the same time mediate between Japan and ourselves.

Please call the President's attention to the fact that the ruthless employment of our submarines now offers the prospect of compelling England in a few months to make peace.

Zimmermann

This extraordinarily compromising cable, which, in effect, offered Mexico the southwestern part of the United States if it would declare war on the United States, was actually handed by Zimmermann to the American Ambassador in Berlin to transmit over the U. S. State Department communications system. Dr. Walter Page, the American Ambassador to England, called this "one of the most audacious and reckless strokes of the war."

Zimmermann knew that nothing would be more likely to infuriate Americans and bring the United States into the war than the publication of his note. He had complete confidence in the safety of the German foreign office cipher.

Unfortunately for Zimmermann, he did not know about Admiral Hall and Room 40. Hall's cryptographers quickly unscrambled what turned out to be by all odds the most important cipher message cracked in World War I. Many historians feel that the cracking of this one cryptogram actually saved the British Empire.

As usual, Admiral Hall was in a quandry. He recognized the enormous importance of the Zimmermann cable, but he also realized the importance of preventing the Germans from learning that their diplomatic cipher had been cracked. The Admiral actually concealed this vital cable from his own government until he had worked out an elaborate system to safeguard the secrets of Room 40. He finally evolved a plan whereby the deciphered cable would be "stolen" by the American counterintelligence authorities either in Mexico or the United States. His deception was so painstakingly elaborated, that even thirty years later, *The Encyclopaedia Britannica* still maintained that the Zimmermann note had been intercepted in the United States.

When the Zimmermann note was released, a storm of rage swept America. President Wilson referred to it when he asked Congress for a declaration of war.

If the Germans had steadfastly denied the existence of the cable and declared it to be a forgery, the British eventually would have been forced to reveal the cipher cable, together with their deciphered copy and the method of decipherment. They could have proved that the cable was genuine, but any such demonstration would have ended the future effectiveness of Admiral Hall and Room 40. By admitting the existence of the cable in a wireless communication, and claiming that it was justified under the circumstances, Zimmermann lost the game.

The cryptographers of Room 40 were very much amused when they decrypted the frantic German cables between Germany, Mexico, and Washington. The enemy did not find out where the fatal leak had occurred until after the war.

In his memoirs, Franz von Papen, who headed German Intelligence activities in Washington, wrote of this affair, "A
great intelligence coup and did us irreparable harm." He also
made the fascinating observation that at the time of the
Zimmermann affair, the Germans had cracked all of the world's
ciphers except those of the English and the Americans.

In a strikingly similar coup, Room 40 untangled the ciphers
of the famous Luxburg telegrams that went back and forth
between Berlin and the German Minister to Argentina. The
German order that the Argentine freighters *Gizo* and *Oran* be
spurlos versenkt (sunk without a trace) horrified South
America and lost Germany that continent.

Admiral Hall and Room 40 experienced their own heart-
breaks, not the least of which was the affair of the German
battle cruiser *Goben*. Both the British and Germans were
doing their best to bring the Ottoman Empire into the war
on their side. Germany had the natural advantage of being
Turkey's closest commercial alley; moreover, the Turks were
outraged because the English had refused to deliver two warships that the Turks had ordered and partly paid for. The
fact that a good part of the money had been raised by popular
subscription in Turkey made the situation all the more touchy.
Britain felt, with some justification, that her own need for
these warships outweighed Turkey's.

In the summer of 1914, the British Mediterranean Fleet was
doing everything in its power to trap the swift new German
battle cruiser *Goben*, which had been caught in the Mediterranean at the outbreak of the war. Aided by its great speed
and by miraculous luck, the *Goben* eluded the British Mediterranean Fleet, and made for the last destination anyone
would have suspected, the Dardanelles.

Recognizing that the Dardanelles were closed to warships,
and knowing that if the *Goben* could not pass through the

Dardanelles defenses, it eventually would be sunk by the pursuing British Fleet, the Germans sold the *Goben* to the Turks by wireless as it was fleeing across the Mediterranean. Thus, suddenly converted into a Turkish war vessel, the mighty battle cruiser, still manned by its German crew, was allowed to penetrate the deadly Dardanelles defenses and proceed across the Sea of Marmora to Constantinople. Now, forty-seven years later, the *Goben,* renamed the *Yavuz* (Strong), is still the pride of the Turkish Navy.

The heartbreak came later, when Room 40 finally cracked one particularly stubborn German cipher. Room 40 went back over all the cables and wireless messages that had been stored up against the day when the cipher would fail. To their horror, the cryptoanalysts found one of August 10, 1914, from Germany to the *Goben:*

> It is of the greatest importance to go to Constantinople as quickly as possible in order thereby to compel Turkey to side with us on the basis of the Treaty that has been concluded. The Ambassador has been informed direct.

Later reasearch showed that between the *Goben* and the Dardanelles, a formidable unit of the British Navy could easily have intercepted and sunk the *Goben,* had the cable been deciphered early enough. If the *Goben* had been intercepted, it is probable that Turkey would not have entered the war on the German side.

The extraordinary intuition that Admiral Hall displayed in his cryptographic work was never more evident than during the last meeting he held with his Room 40 staff at the end of World War I. He concluded his farewell-dinner address with the following words:

Above all we must thank God for our victory over the German nation; and now I want to give you all a word of warning. Hard and bitter as the battle has been, we have now to face a far, far more ruthless foe, a foe that is hydra-headed, and whose evil power will spread over the whole world, and that foe is Russia.

At the time this prophecy was made, Russia was scarcely a country. She had just taken a frightful military beating from Germany, had lost over seven million of her soldiers, had been dismembered by the Treaty of Brest Litovsk, and was undergoing the biggest revolution in history.

As a sad ending to this chapter, Admiral Hall, who possibly did more than any one man to win World War I for the British, received scant recognition for his extraordinary series of coups. The British Army and the Admiralty were reluctant to admit their enormous debt to this remarkable man. History was repeating itself. The German armed forces would not admit their prodigious debt to Bismarck's chief of intelligence, Wilhelm Steiber, and even Bismarck habitually greeted Steiber with his left hand. Similarly, Napoleon Bonaparte never really recognized the tremendous debt he owed to his chief of intelligence, Karl Schulmeister.

10. Cryptanalysis in Espionage

KING PHILIP II of Spain, the haughty monarch who sent the Armada to crush England after Queen Elizabeth I had ordered the execution of Mary, Queen of Scots, did not believe in cryptanalysis. He kept in touch with his tremendous empire—which included not only Spain but also the Netherlands, Belgium, a part of Italy, and most of Central and South America—by use of a cipher in which five hundred symbols stood for the letters of the alphabet.

A few dispatches in this cipher fell into the hands of King Henry IV of France, who turned them over to one of his counselors, the celebrated mathematician François Viète. Viète broke the cipher, and kept right on breaking the new forms of it which turned up in subsequent messages. For two years, the French were able to read any Spanish documents that fell into their hands. After digesting the contents, the French quietly allowed the dispatches to proceed on their way to or from Spain.

When Philip II found out that Viète had cracked his cipher, he demanded that the mathematician be tried in a Papal court on charges of witchcraft, black magic, and trafficking with the Devil. How, demanded Philip, could anyone read his complicated cipher except by raising the spirits of dead men who had used it in their earthly life?

Such was the reputation of cryptographers. A century before, Johannus Trithemius had published the first work in the field of cryptography, only to have his manuscript publicly burned as a piece of magic. The author was lucky not to have shared the fate of his book.

At Philip's request, the Pope duly appointed a commission of cardinals "with urgent recommendation" to investigate Viète's activities. No doubt, the Pope knew more about cryptography than did the King of Spain, and he seems to have been blessed with a sense of humor as well. In any case; the investigations have not been completed to this day. It is possible, though highly unlikely, that the case will some day yet be brought to trial, though it is too late to burn Viète at the stake for witchcraft.

During World War I, the American Government, starting almost from scratch, built up an effective organization for breaking enemy codes and ciphers. Colonel Herbert O. Yardley, its chief, dubbed the new outfit the "American Black Chamber" because the French cryptographic bureau was known as "La Chambre Noire." After the war, Yardley turned his attention to the diplomatic codes and ciphers of other countries, and with his associates, cracked the Japanese secret-writing systems.

Japanese is a unique language. While it may be expressed in ideograms or brush-stroke characters, like Chinese, it may also be written in phonetic symbols like our alphabet, whereby each symbol corresponds to a syllable, not a sound. Thus, a relatively short code book can be used to represent everything in the Japanese language except proper names.

Yardley and his associates attacked the Japanese code with

85

Nov. 28, 1921

Koshi, Washington   URGENT 0073 vrxpm

	dozoorupuh	uteletamme
fuinofridy	uxitupupex	stupesbyuz
uxoyslazij	okecumazij	theveurokul
nhuleadry	eculvoidad	jaeduhpiid
abkiabokij	idjayeokeg	vyodroxmo
ulesamamad	uletefokab	ofokkooaap
zylenyruod	upakotlees	exefaxenaf
hoadazeted	upedasulug	femyacvyhe
ehobbomure	amamouokko	roveivexa-
amowinokny	rueyupakmu	dodojabaiy
ehecdyizny	beupexvevy	panyceoyor
obazebeipn	efaxenafho	adoxvyveid
akedabuluz	cumuenxaro	dohoadenaf
hoadazemda	javyecidk	azulavnyet
upofehijuy	jaoplekole	okinetupbe
izoxnyfouk	enfaipmovu	azijahifvy
nyvyecidko	idewemyeev	ecfiupance
etupihmoku	veevofupek	entuolxaac
vyhimuream	amewexadiz	enteedbudo
mumokeadle	xaenacoyeg	okesobidko
roveivexaz	amowuzdyja	caedkeadin
idhougexaz	amidelfome	Uchida

FIG. 9. *The most famous cipher in American history. Japanese government's instructions to its representatives at the Washington Naval Conference.*

spectacular success, the more remarkable since Yardley could not even speak the language. On November 28, 1921, while

FROM Tokio
TO Washington
Conference No. 13. November 28, 1921.

SECRET

Referring to your cablegram No. 74, we are of your opinion that it is necessary to avoid any clash with Great Britain and America, particularly America, in regard to the armament limitation question. You will to the utmost maintain a middle attitude and redouble your efforts to carry out our policy. In case of inevitable necessity you will work to establish your second proposal of 10 to 6.5. If, in spite of your utmost efforts, it becomes necessary in view of the situation and in the interests of general policy to fall back on your proposal No. 3, you will endeavor to limit the power of concentration and maneuver of the Pacific by a guarantee to reduce or at least to maintain the status quo of Pacific defenses and to make an adequate reservation which will make clear that [this is] our intention in agreeing to a 10 to 6 ratio.

No. 4 is to be avoided as far as possible.

FIG. 10. *Translation of cable in* FIG. 9. *This piece of paper made Japan a second-class Naval power.*

the Washington Naval Conference was in progress, a communication in cipher from the Japanese government to Prince Tokugawa, its representative at the negotiations, was intercepted and turned over to Yardley and his Black Chamber. (See FIG. 9.) It turned out to be one of the most important secret communications in world history, and Yardley succeeded in unscrambling it. (See FIG. 10.) The American cryptographers were able to inform the United States delegation at the conference exactly what secret instructions the Japanese government was sending to its negotiators and the extent to which Japan could be pushed into agreeing to a navy smaller than that of Great Britain and the United States. The decoded cable revealed that if pressed hard enough, the Japanese would agree reluctantly to build only three battleships to every five constructed by the United States and England. This information was all the hard-nosed American and British negotiators needed to put Japan in a subordinate position.

Seven years later, in the spirit of world-wide disarmament and treaties by which countries promised not to make war, the American Government decided to scrap its cryptographic department and stop reading other countries' secret messages entirely. Colonel Yardley found himself out of a job. He turned his talents to writing a book, *The American Black Chamber*, in which he told the whole story of America's success with cryptanalysis, including the background of the Washington Naval Conference. This irresponsible book badly damaged the United States and indirectly cost many Americans their lives.

Publication of *The American Black Chamber* so outraged the Japanese, that the government in Tokyo fell, and a wave of anti-Americanism swept the country. The two nations had never been at war and had been "friendly" at the time of the disarmament conference. The Japanese militarists declared that they wanted no further part in tricky treaties limiting the size of their navy and they began to lay the keels of the ships that fought against the United States in World War II. Some of these, such as the *Yamato* and *Musashi*, were the largest warships ever built by any country. Meanwhile, in the growing tension of the prewar years from 1933 to 1941, the United

States quietly re-established an organization to break the codes and ciphers of potential enemies. Today, this outfit is known as the National Security Agency. It was established in its present form by a presidential directive in 1952. Insiders will tell you that the initials "NSA" stand for "Never say anything."

In World War II, our code-crackers identified themselves by the code name MAGIC. Like the work of the French cryptographer Viète, what they did seemed like black magic. When it became known to some of our Congressmen that MAGIC had indeed furnished the intelligence that could have prevented the disaster at Pearl Harbor (See Chapter 18), a committee aired the whole matter publicly. If it had not been for this investigation, little now would be known about MAGIC's existence and the part it played in the war. The congressional inquiries brought to light the fact that American and British cryptanalysts had been co-operating closely. Together they cracked the code used by Japanese military attachés in all parts of the world.

Unfortunately, such close teamwork was not matched among American intelligence organizations. Unaware of MAGIC's work, OSS agents broke into the Japanese mission in Lisbon and stole a copy of the very code book that already had been so laboriously cracked. To the consternation of the Americans and British, the Japanese government abruptly stopped using the stolen code.

This one OSS raid cut off one of the Allies' best sources of information in World War II and gave one of the authors of this book, at that time the OSS liaison with the Navy Cryptographic Bureau, some of his worst headaches of the war. An immediate order went out to all the Allied spy and counterspy services to the effect that no code book ever was to be stolen without prior authorization. Any agent who came across a code book while breaking into an enemy office was to try to erase all evidence that the office had been entered, and to await further orders.

Other interesting sidelights on inter-Allied co-operation— or the lack if it—came to light before another Congressional committee, which was investigating Communist spying in the United States. Although America and Russia were allies in World War II, the Reds maintained a large and active spy network in this country before, during, and after the war. When Elizabeth Bentley, who confessed openly that she had served the Russians as a spy in our State Department, took the stand to tell how she had turned information over to the Reds, she claimed that she had warned the Russians near the end of the war that MAGIC was about to reveal the contents of some of their secret messages. Of course, her Communist bosses wanted to know which code or cipher of theirs the Americans were breaking, but she was unable to find out anything further.

This dream of perfect U.S. cryptographic security was rudely shattered in June of 1960. Two young mathematicians, William H. Martin and Vernon F. Mitchell, who worked for the National Security Agency, went on vacation to Mexico. They left their hotel secretly, made their way to Castro's Cuba, and embarked on a Russian submarine. When next heard from, they were in Russia, seeking Russian citizenship, and shouting to all the world that America was trying to read the secret messages of friendly countries. The damage they have caused America undoubtedly is substantial.

The National Security Agency is now located in a $35-million-dollar air-conditioned installation at Fort Meade, halfway between Washington and Baltimore. It employs some fifteen thousand people. About one-third of its $120-million-dollar budget goes into research and equipment. Making and breaking codes and ciphers is an expensive business.

Employes are rigidly screened. Only about four thousand out of eighteen thousand applicants have obtained jobs there in the course of the last three years. Although the agency needs specialists in all languages, from Annamese to Tibetan, no one who is not a natural-born citizen of the United States can qualify. The reason is obvious: our potential enemies have been known to use the most brutal forms of torture on relatives of naturalized Americans whom they want to force into becoming their spies.

Following the defection of Martin and Mitchell, worse was yet to come. In May, 1960, the Russians abruptly canceled the projected "summit" meeting between Khrushchev and Eisenhower. The Russians had just succeeded in shooting down an American reconnaissance plane flying over the heart of Russia. The very existence of the U-2, that eerie, wide-winged plane capable of flying at the incredible altitude of 100,000 feet and over a range of thousands of miles, previously had been unknown to the public. It has been suggested that sabotage wrecked the oxygen equipment of the unlucky plane, forcing it down to 30,000 feet, where it was a relatively easy mark for Russian missiles. Another theory, more unlikely, is that the Russians secretly developed a super-high-altitude interceptor plane that brought it down.

The U-2 flights over Russia have not been resumed. One of their missions, in addition to photographing large and inaccessible areas of the earth's surface, was to bring back recordings of Russian radio broadcasts, both in plain language and in cipher. The tapes were sent to the National Security Agency. It is likely that the NSA also studies carefully the beep-beeps of the Sputniks.

No secret information is worth much unless a country has the will and the power to act on it. America put Yardley's work to good use in 1922, but all of MAGIC's success failed to prevent the Japanese surprise attack on Pearl Harbor. The clutch between the engine and the wheels appeared to be missing.

After Pearl Harbor, the United States again was able to act decisively. Four of the Japanese carriers that had attacked Pearl Harbor were sunk six months later at Midway. From the information based on Japanese messages, our admirals were convinced that the main attack would come at Midway. The Japanese sent a task force to bomb Dutch Harbor in the hope of diverting our attention to Alaska, but the United States Navy knew better than to abandon its post near Midway. The disgrace of Pearl Harbor was wiped out, and the man who planned it, Admiral Yamamoto, was shot down in flames over Kahili a year later.

Secret intelligence is no better than its practical application. A fate like Yamamoto's might have befallen an American President if the Nazis had had a different translator for a certain job. When Roosevelt and Churchill decided to meet at Casablanca in North Africa in 1943, Spanish spies in Washington got wind of the plan, and word was sent to Hitler. In translating the deciphered Spanish-language message, however, an eager-beaver German failed to recognize "Casablanca" as a place name, and read it as two Spanish words, *casa* and *blanca*. The message said that the Allied leaders planned to meet, not in Casablanca but at the White House. Washington was out of range for Nazi planes, and Roosevelt and Churchill escaped attack.

11. Some Nazi Stratagems

IF American intelligence agencies sometimes acted at cross-purposes in World War II, so did some of America's enemies. In the dark days of 1941 and 1942, it seemed to the rest of the world that Hitler's war machine functioned with precision-tooled, monolithic perfection, but this was hardly the case, especially in the crucial field of cryptanalysis.

With the outbreak of war, the section of the Reich Security Service that was concerned with political intelligence (spying in foreign countries) passed under military control. Its chief was Colonel Schellenberg. Meanwhile, the old guard tried to maintain the independence of its own military intelligence unit under Admiral Canaris. Ribbentrop's Foreign Office maintained a staff to work over intercepted Allied diplomatic telegrams, and Marshal Goering of the Luftwaffe established a "Research Office," supposedly an independent organization, to collect its own material, carry on cryptanalysis, and co-ordinate the work of the others. With so many agencies competing for Hitler's favor and each one jealously guarding its source of information, confusion was inevitable.

Colonel Wilhelm Hoettl, who before the war, had joined the Reich Security Service as a Balkan expert, discovered that General Figl, the Austro-Hungarian Empire's crack cryptanalyst during World War I, had been arrested by the Gestapo in 1938. Hoettl succeeded in springing Figl from prison and established him in a villa at Wannsee, in Berlin, where he taught cryptography to a new generation of Germans.

On a visit to Budapest in 1942, Hoettl was taken to see the Hungarian Radio Interception Unit, a modest outfit with little equipment, which nonetheless produced excellent results from the limited material in its hands. So devoted to cryptanalysis was its chief, Major Bibo, that he scrimped money from his meager officer's salary to purchase supplies at his own expense.

Impressed by the fact that the Hungarians were doing better than the Nazis themselves, and disturbed also because they were keeping out of German hands some of the best intelligence their cryptanalysts were producing, Hoettl took Major Bibo to a small Budapest café and suggested a deal: The Germans would finance the construction of more powerful intercept stations and provide other necessary equipment if Bibo would concentrate on problems of greatest interest to the Nazis. When Hoettl went over the head of Bibo's infuriated chief to obtain secret consent from Prime Minister Sztojay himself, the Hungarian agreed.

Armed with the excellent information that the Hungarians supplied, Hoettl then laid the plan before Schellenberg, the Nazi intelligence chief. Schellenberg was enthusiastic about this new pipeline of information, but he refused point-blank to underwrite the German side of the deal—the Fuehrer didn't trust the Hungarians. Schellenberg told Hoettl that he could go as far as he liked with the funds already at his disposal, but not to expect a *pfennig* from his chief.

Hoettl did exactly as the boss told him. Characteristically, his superior had no idea of either the amount or the extent of Hoettl's fiscal power. With an initial kitty of one hundred thousand Swiss francs, Hoettl, set about beefing up Hungary's interception and cryptanalysis, concentrating especially on getting all the radio traffic moving to and from Allied and neutral embassies in Russia. According to Hoettl, one of the Hungarian cryptanalysts was possessed of such intuition, that he could sense which message, from a big sheaf of intercepted telegrams, carried the most important information.

The brilliant Hungarians found that the French were still using codes, and they achieved considerable success in cracking them. Britain and the United States employed methods of much greater security, which, Hoettl concluded, must be at least in part, machine systems.

For sheer information, the best source of all proved to be Turkish telegrams. Some of the most significant intelligence that the Turks uncovered in Moscow, and which Hoettl decoded and read through the good offices of the Hungarians, concerned Stalin's mistrust of his American and British allies. The Russian dictator was apparently obsessed with the nightmare that Churchill and Roosevelt would conclude a separate peace with Germany. He would have been startled, indeed, if he had been able to look ahead to 1962 and see his successor threatening the Western powers with the same nightmare.

Hoettl assessed the Turkish diplomats as being especially perspicacious political reporters, and he thought the translations of coded Turkish diplomatic messages furnished the Germans with more and better information than their own ambassador could uncover in Ankara. This is most surprising since Germany's ambassador to Turkey was none other than the wily Franz von Papen, who had intrigued in World War I with the Mexican government to embroil the United States with Japan, as revealed by the publication of the Zimmermann

Note. In World War II, the foxy old diplomat was sent to Ankara with the delicate mission of keeping Turkey from joining the Allies.

Von Papen had an incomparable intelligence pipeline in Ankara through the activities of Mr. Bazna, the Albanian valet of the British Ambassador. Bazna, better known by his German code name of CICERO, made it a constant practice to rifle the Embassy safe of important documents, photographs and replace them, and pass the copies on to Moyzisch, an SS officer attached to the German Embassy. For this unique service, CICERO was paid handsomely—well over a million dollars. Unfortunately for him, the money was counterfeit.

Transcripts of the minutes of the Teheran Conference, at which Stalin, Roosevelt, and Churchill met to discuss top-level strategy, and also of the Cairo Conference, passed through CICERO's hands into those of the Nazis.

With exact copies of original British documents, the Germans should have been able to match the plain text of messages with the coded telegrams to and from London, and break all the top British diplomatic systems. Perhaps the British were skillful and painstaking paraphrasers; perhaps their systems were so secure that, even with such "ponies," the Germans could get nowhere, or perhaps the German intelligence agencies were working at such cross-purposes that they failed completely to turn over to their own cryptanalytic units the information CICERO provided.

In any case, Hitler was stubbornly skeptical of the authenticity of any intelligence indicative of growing enemy strength, and the British cryptographic systems appear to have remained secure.

Both CICERO and the Hungarian cryptanalysts sources were financed through Operation BERNHARD, the top-secret Nazi program devoted to the counterfeiting of Allied currency, especially English pounds, by engravers who were prisoners in a German concentration camp. The "funny money" was good enough to fool any but the most careful inspectors. Hitler counted on it to wreck enemy economies. Both the one hundred thousand Swiss francs with which Hoettl launched his Hungarian scheme, and the money paid out to CICERO, came from credits in a Swiss bank based on payment in forged notes. When United States investigators, examined the files of Admiral Canaris' *Abwehr* (Naval Intelligence) after the war, they were horrified to discover that the *Abwehr* had been in possession of complete plans for our invasion of North Africa long before it took place. Intelligence information had been fed through the various German espionage organizations to the top intelligence echelon, run by General Nicolai, who had also been the head of German intelligence in World War I.

Evidently, Himmler was so outraged at the magnificent coup pulled by the rival Canaris organization, that he actually had suppressed the information of the North African landing at General Nicolai's level. If it had ever reached the German General Staff, the United States could easily have suffered a worse defeat than Pearl Harbor.

12. How to Crack a Substitution Cipher

AFTER a dinner party, a clever host once startled his guests by asking his wife to go out of the room. While she was gone, he asked the others to select the name of a world-famous person. When the wife returned, he said, "Darling, our plans for our drive south are quite simple. We'll go to Roanoke on the second day and then drive on to Daytona." The wife looked at her husband happily. "You are thinking of Nikita Khrushchev," she said.

The amazed guests picked another famous name, and when the wife returned, her husband said, "Darling, I'm not looking forward to my next sales trip. All over Pennsylvania for four days and then to Louisiana for thirty-four days." The wife looked at the guests smugly. "It's Franklin Delano Roosevelt," she said quickly. She was right.

One of the guests asked to hear the husband's statements repeated exactly. He listened carefully and then said he was ready to try it. The others chose ex-President Eisenhower. When the guest returned, the host said, "I hear that on your next vacation you are planning to go to Georgia and spend four days at Lake Franklin." "It's Ike!" announced the guest.

The guest had figured out a sort of enciphered code that his host and hostess used. The host did not try to convey the celebrity's name, but instead chose a short word suggesting his identity. The consonants of this expression were not enciphered, but were indicated by the first letters of the geographic spots he mentioned. The numbers of days were substituted for the vowels, "1, 2, 3, 4, and 5," representing "A, E, I, O, and U," in that matching order. When the husband said, "We'll get to Roanoke on the second and then drive to Daytona," he was spelling the word RED. The most famous "Red" of course is Nikita Khrushchev. His second sentence spelled out "polio," which immediately suggested Franklin Delano Roosevelt. The guest caught onto his system and recognized in turn, Ike from the word "golf."

There is really very little magic and a lot of brain work in the breaking of ciphers. It requires practice, hard work, the use of frequency tables, and that mysterious sense of excitement that makes people enjoy solving puzzles.

Suppose that a message reads:

FXXM FX TM LBQ BG MAX KHHF HOXK MAX ZTKTZX.

It can be seen almost at a glance that this is not a simple transposition, like the ciphers in Chapters 3 and 4, because such letters as X, K, and F do not appear so frequently in ordinary language. The message, therefore, must be a substitution.

The simplest type of substitution is the Julius Caesar variety. The trick is to "run down the alphabet" with the first eight or ten letters of the message. If one of the lines produced in the run is readable as plain language, the cipher must be Caesar's. By counting the letter interval, the rest of the message can be read easily without writing any more laborious columns of letters:

Cipher:									
1	F	X	X	M	F	X	T	M
2	G	Y	Y	N	G	Y	U	N
3	H	Z	Z	O	H	Z	V	O
4	I	A	A	P	I	A	W	P
5	J	B	B	Q	J	B	X	Q
6	K	C	C	R	K	C	Y	R
7	L	D	D	S	L	D	Z	S
8	M	E	E	T	M	E	A	T
9	N	F	F	U	N	F	B	U
10	O	G	G	V	O	G	C	V
11	P	H	H	W	P	H	D	W
12	Q	I	I	X	Q	I	E	X
13	R	J	J	Y	R	J	F	Y
14	S	K	K	Z	S	K	G	Z
15	T	L	L	A	T	L	H	A
16	U	M	M	B	U	M	I	B
17	V	N	N	C	V	N	J	C
18	W	O	O	D	W	O	K	D
19	X	P	P	E	X	P	L	E
20	Y	Q	Q	F	Y	Q	M	F
21	Z	R	R	G	Z	R	N	G
22	A	S	S	H	A	S	O	H
23	B	T	T	I	B	T	P	I
24	C	U	U	J	C	U	Q	J
25	D	V	V	K	D	V	R	K
26	E	W	W	L	E	W	S	L

Line 18 started off promisingly with WOOD, but WO and KD are meaningless. Clearly, the beginning of the message must be Line 8, MEET ME AT.

You can run down the alphabet much more quickly by

writing alphabets vertically on strips of graph paper and shifting them up and down so that the cipher message appears horizontally. The process becomes even more efficient when the vertical strips are two alphabets in length. Then there is no danger of running out of room on one strip before the proper line is reached.

In general, longer cipher messages are easier to solve than shorter ones. This rule does not hold true with the Julius Caesar cipher. By running down the alphabet, you can break a message only a few letters long. You often can break a very short transposition cipher, if the "box" is small enough, because a few letters may be anagrammed into words much more easily than a large number of letters.

There is no mechanical method quite as satisfactory as running down the alphabet for solving substitutions in which the cipher alphabet is mixed up, instead in normal sequence. Nevertheless, simple substitutions are not much more difficult to solve, especially if the word divisions are shown.

In Edgar Allan Poe's "The Gold Bug," pirate treasure is discovered through the cracking of a simple substitution in which numbers and printer's marks (†, ‡, *, and the like) are substituted for letters. The eccentric islander who breaks Captain Kidd's message uses the letter-frequency method.

Almost everyone knows that E is the commonest of all letters used—constituting 12 per cent of written English. Careful studies have been made of different kinds of writing, especially telegraphic messages (in which articles are usually omitted, to determine the frequency with which letters appear. If the cipher message is long enough—say several pages—the commonest letter will be E, the next T, and so forth.

FIG. 11 shows the order of frequency in English of all the letters of the alphabet, and also how often each letter appears in a thousand words. FIG. 12 lists the most common English

LETTER FREQUENCY IN ENGLISH

Letter	Frequency Per 1000 Letters	Letter	Frequency Per 1000 Letters	Letter	Frequency Per 1000 Letters
E	131	D	38	W	15
T	105	L	34	B	14
A	82	F	29	V	9
O	80	C	28	K	4
N	71	M	25	X	2—
R	68	U	25	J	1+
I	63	G	20	Q	1+
S	61	Y	20	Z	.7+
H	53	P	20		

FIG. 11

words in the order of their frequency. The average English word is four and a half letters long. If a message is over two hundred words, the average in these frequency tables become increasingly accurate. (See FIG. 13 for more frequency tables useful in cryptographic work.)

Even a message that is too short to reveal absolute letter frequency can be solved. Nearly three hundred years ago, in 1674, the Chevalier De Rohan conspired to sell out the fortress of Quilleboeuf, which he commanded. The only other man on the French side who knew of his plot was his aide, La Trouaumont, who was as deeply involved as his master. French counterintelligence agents, however, began to suspect a plot. One night, while De Rohan was awaiting the return of his aide from the enemy lines, a shot rang out. La Trouaumont was wounded, and De Rohan was arrested at once.

His friends were able to inform him that only the wounded man's evidence might be used against him. On the morning of his trial, they smuggled in a cipher message, pinned to the

MOST COMMON ENGLISH WORDS
Frequency Per 10000 Words

the	420	not	22	being	10	now	6
of	222	were	20	its	10	people	6
and	142	or	19	no	10	public	6
to	132	all	18	only	10	said	6
in	111	their	18	over	10	since	6
a	108	an	16	very	10	still	6
is	72	I	16	you	10	such	6
that	61	there	15	into	9	through	6
be	43	been	14	most	9	under	6
it	43	many	14	than	9	up	6
by	42	more	14	they	9	war	6
are	40	so	14	day	8	well	6
for	40	when	14	even	8	where	6
was	32	had	13	made	8	while	6
as	31	may	13	out	8	years	6
he	31	today	13	first	7	before	5
with	31	who	13	great	7	between	5
on	30	would	13	must	7	country	5
his	29	time	12	these	7	debts	5
at	25	we	12	can	6	good	5
which	25	about	11	days	6	him	5
but	24	after	11	every	6	interest	5
from	24	dollars	11	found	6	large	5
has	24	if	11	general	6	like	5
this	24	my	11	her	6	make	5
will	24	other	11	here	6	our	5
one	23	some	11	last	6	take	5
have	22	them	11	new	6	upon	5
						what	5

FIG. 12

ORDER OF FREQUENCIES

Digraphs	Tri-graphs	Doubles	First Letters	Last Letters	Two-Letter Words	Three-Letter Words	Four-Letter Words
th	the	ss	T	E	of	the	that
er	and	ee	O	S	to	and	with
on	tha	tt	A	T	in	for	have
an	ent	ff	W	D	it	are	this
re	ion	ll	B	N	is	but	will
he	tio	mm	C	R	be	not	your
in	for	oo	D	Y	as	you	from
ed	nde		S	F	at	all	they
nd	has		F	L	so	any	know
ha	nce		M	O	we	can	want
at	edt		R	G	he	had	been
en	tis		H	H	by	her	good
es	oft		I	A	or	was	much
of	sth		Y	K	on	one	some
or	men		E	M	do	our	time
nt			G	P	if	out	very
ea			L	U	me	day	when
ti			N	W	my	get	come
to			P		up	has	here
it			U		an	him	just
io			J		go	his	like
le			K		no	how	long
is					us	man	make
ou					am	new	many
ar						now	more
as						old	only
de						see	over
rt						two	such
ve						way	take
						who	than
						boy	them

ORDER OF FREQUENCIES

Digraphs	Tri-graphs	Doubles	First Letters	Last Letters	Two-Letter Words	Three-Letter Words	Four-Letter Words
						did	well
						its	were
						let	
						put	
						say	
						she	
						too	
						use	

FIG. 13

sleeve of a clean shirt in his laundry. De Rohan had often boasted of his ability to crack cryptograms, but he could make nothing of the jumble of letters on which his life depended. When brought to trial, he confessed everything and begged for mercy. The court had little pity for traitors, and De Rohan was beheaded.

What did the message say? With the original text translated into English, it read: SYL FRB XT QLRQ YL QXQ BGS TRH RBHSYXBO NLMGAL YL QXLQ.

The first thing De Rohan should have done, once he was certain this was a substitution other than a Caesar cipher, was to make a chart showing the frequency of each letter. This is done easily by tally:

```
                     —
       —             —          —
  —                  —        — —            — —
  —                  —      — — —            — —
  —          — —     —    — — — —            — —
— —        — — —   — — — —    — — — —        — —
A B C D E F G H I J K L M N O P Q R S T U V W X Y Z
```

Another more useful kind of count shows not only the frequency of letters, but indicates which letters usually appear before and after them. This type of chart helps to spot repetitions:

```
                                        X–Q
                                        Y–
                                        A–
        X–O                             N–M
        R–H                             Y–
         –G                 M–A  B–      Q–R
G–L  R–              –R   B–S  R–         Y–        L–G   –L
A       B    C  D  E  F     G      H I J K  L            M    N


        L–
        –X
        X–       –B                     Q–L    –L
        –X   T–H  –Y                    Y–B    S–X
        R–    –Q  G–  –R                Q–Q    –L
B–      –L    F–B  –Y X–                 –T    S–L
O  P    Q     R    S  T  U V W           X    Y    Z
```

CONTACT CHART

Since L is the commonest letter in the ciphered message, it may represent E:

```
.    SYL FRB XT QLRQ YL QXQ BGS TRH
      e            e        e
     RBHSYXBO NLMGAL YL QXLQ
            e       e   e      e
```

If this is correct, then "e" occurs twice in a two-letter word as the second letter. Is the word YL "be"? (See FIG. 12.) This is unlikely, as Y appears more frequently (four times in all) than one would expect "b" to occur. The next two-letter word ending in "e" is "he." Y may be "h." Then the first word, "he," is probably "the." This is confirmed, since "th," a common-letter pair, appears in the longest word.

SYL FRB XT QLRQ YL QXQ BGS TRH
the   e   he   t

RBHSYXBO NLMGAL YL QXLQ
th   e   e he   e

Q is the second most common letter in the message. T is the second most common letter in English (See fig. 11), but a value has already been assigned to "t." Could Q be the third highest, "a"? This would give us three words ending in "a," unlikely except as proper names. O is out for the same reason. Q apparently stands for a consonant. Substituting "n" for Q would give "n-n" perhaps? But "non" is almost hopeless for QXLQ, and "ne-n" is worse for QLRQ. Equally impossible are "r" and "s." How about "d"? "D-d" suggests did," and QXLQ then becomes "died."

With QXLQ as "died," QLRQ is a good bet for "dead." Then the message reads:

SYL FRB XT QLRQ YL QXQ BGS TRH
The   a   i   dead   he   did   t   a

RBHSYXBO NLMGAL YL QXLQ
a   thi   e   e he   died

It begins to look like "the man is dead . . ."

SYL FRB XT QLRQ YL QXQ BGS TRH
The   man   is   dead   he   did   n   t   sa

RBHSYXBO NLMGAL YL QXLQ
a   n   thin   e   e he   died

At this point, one can guess the letters faster than they can be written down. RBHSYXBO must be "anything," and this is confirmed by TRH as "say." NLMGAL is "before."

If the treacherous Chevalier had been smarter, he would have cracked this simple cipher and kept his head on his shoulders by keeping his mouth shut.

A more cheerful example concerns Professor George Beadle. In 1958, while he was the Eastman Professor of Chemistry at Oxford University in England, Dr. Beadle (California Institute of Technology) received the most coveted honor that can be bestowed on a research scientist. He was named, together with two associates, as winner of the Nobel Prize in medicine. They had demonstrated that the genes, those tiny units in a cell's nucleus that govern heredity, actually contain a sort of coded message to control the chemical processes of the next generation.

When news of his honor was published, Professor Beadle's friends all over the world inundated him with cablegrams of congratulation. One of the messages from California never would have passed wartime restrictions. It consisted of two solid pages in cipher. It undoubtedly cost Beadle's well-wisher a sizable sum to send such a cable to England, and it took the brilliant professor forty hours of tough mental gymnastics to decipher it.

Since the message expressed in the chemical formulae the four units of nucleic acid that compose the genes (See Chapter 28), Dr. Beadle knew at once that it was the work of one of his Caltech colleagues. Having converted the weird scientific notation into the letters of the English alphabet, Beadle was faced with a second substitution problem. The chemist proved himself a competent cryptanalyst, and found himself admonished, BREAK THIS CODE OR GIVE BACK NOBEL

PRIZE. Like many other people, Beadle's friend didn't know a "code" from a cipher.

Anyone who works with ciphers knows that it is helpful to set up the deciphering alphabet as he goes along. This often will uncover the system used and save the cryptographer much work. To return a moment to the cipher of the unfortunate Chevalier De Rohan—at one point, the alphabet for our De Rohan case would be,

Cipher: ABCDEFGHIJKLMNOPQRSTUVWXYZ
Plain: r n   l m y   e f   d a t s   i h

An alert cryptographer instantly would notice that S (cipher) is "t" (plain) and T (cipher) is "s" (plain). H and Y can be interchanged in the same way. The alphabets appear to be what is called "reciprocal." A (cipher) should be "r" (plain), and M (cipher) should be "f" (plain). The remainder of the message is obvious.

Reciprocal alphabets are especially convenient, because when you encipher a letter, you won't turn up the wrong equivalent by letting your eye stray to the cipher line first. Unfortunately, reciprocal alphabets also make solution easier.

Several facts emerge from this solution, and others may be worked out easily:

(1). Frequency charts are necessary, but they are not absolutely reliable for assigning letter values except in very long messages.

(2). Combinations of letters are important. Some pairs may be reversed, as DE and ED, ON and NO, RE and ER, or TH and HT, but others may not be. NT is much more common than TN, and UQ is practically an impossible combination. Likewise some letters double easily, like EE, SS, OO, and TT, while II and WW almost never occur.

(3). Short words are helpful, since they must contain vowels. (In the professional use of ciphers, however, the message is usually divided into five-letter groups. This masks all word divisions.)

(4). Establishing the value of consonants is much more helpful in determining the message than the solution of vowels.

(5). "Pattern" words are especially valuable. "Bookkeeping," with the only triple sequence of doubled letters in English, is an extreme example. The pattern of "bookkeeping" can be expressed as "abbccddefgh." This word does not often appear in ciphers, but the alert cryptographer learns to spot the patterns of such words as "letter" (abccbd), "mission" (abccbde), "decoded" (abceaba), and many more.

(6). Proper names, and other words likely to appear in a given message ("jewels," or "agent," and the like), may enable you to break a simple substitution cipher almost without effort.

(7). In some instances, it is possible to guess at the key of the cipher alphabet. Few people can memorize twenty-six letters and their cipher equivalents. For this reason, most cipher alphabets are constructed from a long word or phrase that is easy to remember. First, any repeated letters are deleted, and then the alphabet is completed with the leftover letters. If the key were JAZZ CONCERT, for example, the cipher alphabet would be constructed as follows:

JAZz CONcERT

Plain: ABCDEFGHIJKLMNOPQRSTUVWXYZ
Cipher: JAZCONERTBDFGHIKLMPQSUVWXY

The cryptographer may be able to reconstruct a key such as this by doing some clever guessing after he has established the value of a handful of letters.

(8). The more the cryptographer knows about the people

whose mail he is trying to read, the better his chances are of solving their ciphers quickly.

An organization whose members must keep in touch through secret writing should have its own cryptographic department. This department should keep sharp by solving cryptograms as puzzles, and cracking the messages of competing organizations. A head cryptographer would be able to solve rapidly such messages as the one at the end of this chapter.

The cryptogram puzzles in newspapers are scarcely a fair test. They are deliberately designed to upset frequency counts by using such words as "icthyology" or "syzygy," and they specialize in sentences in which every word begins with the same letter. In other words, the plain text means almost as little as the cipher.

Rules for Cracking Any Simple Substitution Cipher:

1. Run down the alphabet; it could be a Caesar cipher.

2. Make a frequency distribution chart; a contact chart that shows repetitions and reversals of letters is the most useful.

3. Mark repetitions and reversals.

4. Be on the lookout for pattern words and for any words that the correspondents are likely to use.

5. Try assigning the value of the high-frequency letters, E-T-A-O-N, *et cetera*, to the letters that appear most frequently.

6. Use the assumed letters to puzzle out words with other letters.

7. Reconstruct the enciphering alphabet, keeping an eye out for possible reciprocal alphabets, or for key word sequences.

Solve this sample message, and recover the key. (To check for a key word, write the letters of the plain message in alphabetical order, with the cipher letters under them):

IHT IO QAT OMLNQ QCNDN QI RT
PIHT MH NIEUMHG NTYLTQ FTNNCGTN
MN QI YISHQ QAT ETQQTL OLTKSTHYMTN

Make some alphabet strips and use them to solve the following messages in the Julius Caesar cipher:
1. FIMRK WLEHSAIH
2. COXKY ZGVVKJ
3. ACJJ KCCRGLE RMKMPPMU YR DPYLIQ FMSQC
4. VMML UWZM UWVMG NWZ AIJWBIOM
The solution of the sample message reads,
ONE OF THE FIRST TASKS TO BE DONE IN SOLVING SECRET MESSAGES IS TO COUNT THE LETTER FREQUENCIES
Key: CRYPTOG(R)AM

The messages in the Julius Caesar cipher are:
1. BEING SHADOWED
2. WIRES TAPPED
3. CELL MEETING TOMORROW AT FRANK'S HOUSE
4. NEED MORE MONEY FOR SABOTAGE

13. How to Clobber
the Antique Dealer

EVERYONE has had the experience of going into an antique or secondhand store and looking at the tag on an article, only to find an incomprehensible cipher like B Y S O or L B H. The shopkeeper looks at the tag and quickly tells the customer the price will be $65.42 for the article marked B Y S O and $1.60 for the one marked L B H.

The "Shopkeeper's Cipher" can be so arranged as to give the shopkeeper the price at which he purchased the article, the sales price, the year it came into the shop, and almost any other pertinent data. It is usually based on a ten-letter word or phrase in which none of the letters repeat. The key to the cipher used by the storekeeper in the above case was:

$$\begin{array}{cccccccccc} L & O & U & S & Y & B & A & T & C & H \\ 1 & 2 & 3 & 4 & 5 & 6 & 7 & 8 & 9 & 0. \end{array}$$

When keyed in, the B Y S O totals $65.42, while the L B H becomes $1.60.

Antique dealers often use the cipher on an article so that they will know how much leeway they have for bargaining.

A customer who can crack a shopkeeper's cipher obviously has an enormous advantage in haggling with him.

One of the authors decided to crack the cipher of his favorite antique dealer. He started by copying the tag symbols on a number of articles and asking the dealer the selling price. He then put together the following table:

Article	Price Quoted by Shopkeeper	Tag Symbol
1. Bookstand	$ 90.00	P Y G I
2. Old Print	167.00	F F A I
3. Persian Bowl	30.00	G G Y F
4. Samurai Sword	55.00	I G S P
5. Turkish Kutiah Plate	14.50	Y R U
6. French Clock	230.00	U P I S
7. Bronze Figure	810.00	P S P F I
8. Inlaid Box	31.00	G I Y F
9. Egyptian Bracelet	8.20	P I F

He took the list home and got out his slide rule. It was obvious at once that if this were a simple shopkeeper's cipher, like the one based on L O U S Y B A T C H above, the symbols did not apply to the retail prices of the articles because the letters did not match. The old print price started with the digit 1 as did the price for the Turkish Kutiah plate. The first letter of the first tag symbol was F; the first letter of the second one was Y. On the other hand, the digit 1 in the price of the inlaid box was the symbol I. Obviously, the cipher did not give the retail price.

Our detective decided to assume that the cipher denoted the cost price. He also calculated that inasmuch as all of the articles came from the sale of the effects of one estate, the markup of sales price over costs would be approximately the same for all of the articles. If he once got the cipher worked out, it would apply to everything else in the shop, no matter what the markup.

He decided to tackle the problem on the basis of finding the markup that would make the figures and the symbols fit each other. The storekeeper gave the sales price so swiftly after looking at the cipher that the author decided the markup must be simple enough to decipher without pencil and paper. He decided to try two markups, one 100 per cent over the cost, and the second, 150 per cent over the cost, to see what would happen.

He added two more columns on the right side of the chart; the first one represented the cost at 100 per cent markup; the second column showed the cost at 150 per cent markup. To arrive at the figures in the first new column, our cipher expert divided the cost prices by two; in the second column, he divided them by $2\frac{1}{2}$. The table now looked like this:

Article	Price Quoted by Shopkeeper	Tag Symbol	Cost Price at 100% Markup	Cost Price at 150% Markup
1. Bookstand	$ 90.00	P Y G I	$ 45.00	$ 36.00
2. Old Print	167.00	F F A I	83.50	67.00
3. Persian Bowl	30.00	G G Y F	15.00	12.00
4. Samurai Sword	55.00	I G S P	27.50	22.50
5. Turkish Kutiah Plate	14.50	Y R U	7.25	5.80
6. French Clock	230.00	U P I S	115.00	92.00
7. Bronze Figure	810.00	P S P F I	405.00	324.00
8. Inlaid Box	31.00	G I Y F	15.50	12.40
9. Egyptian Bracelet	8.20	P I F	4.10	3.28

Depending upon the markup, the P in the P Y G I cipher of Article 1, the bookstand, must be either 3 or 4. The first P in the cipher for the Egyptian bracelet is also 3 or 4.

The fact that nearly all of the quoted prices were nice even numbers meant that the storekeeper did not apply his markup exactly but rounded it off, usually to the nearest dollar. The digit 3 appeared to be more probable than 4, since (1) the markup was more likely to be 150 per cent, and (2) 3.5 (the average of 3 and 4) did not come as close to the cost price of the bookstand, the bronze figure, and the Egyptian bracelet when it was marked up 100 per cent as it did when marked up 150 per cent.

Thus, our expert shopper arrived at the reasonable conclusion that P was 3 and that the markup was somewhere around 150 per cent for this particular batch of merchandise:

$$1\ 2\ 3\ 4\ 5\ 6\ 7\ 8\ 9\ 0$$
$$P$$

Since P was the only letter he could link with $30, he put it tentatively under the 3. Obviously, this was only a start. If the markup of the Persian bowl were anything between 50 per cent and 200 per cent, the first figure of the original cost would have to be 1. Therefore, he was practically certain that G was 1:

$$1\ 2\ 3\ 4\ 5\ 6\ 7\ 8\ 9\ 0$$
$$G\quad P$$

The author knew that the first figure of each cipher group is the most significant one to work with because it is the least subject to change. He knew that by merely rounding off the sales price to an even number, he would throw out completely the last figure in the cipher, and possibly the figure to the left of it. The first digit would seldom be affected.

The author decided to approximate all of the first digits by dividing the cost figures by 2½ and paying attention only to the first digit of the result. These figures are in the last column. The F in the old print is 6; the G in the Persian bowl is 1; the I in the Samurai sword is 2; the Y in the Turkish Kutiah plate is 5; the U in the French clock is 9, and the 3 in the bronze figure is P. Once the first figures had been developed, the second signicant figures were much more difficult because they were ten times more inaccurate.

The Turkish Kutiah plate and its second significant figure gave our man R as 7, and the bronze figure gave S as 4. His tally looked like this:

$$1\ 2\ 3\ 4\ 5\ 6\ 7\ 8\ 9\ 0$$
$$G\ I\ P\ S\ Y\ F\ R\ A\ U\ D$$

It is easy now to uncover the antique dealer's key word— GIPSY FRAUD. He was obviously a man with a sense of humor. There are undoubtedly many quicker ways to solve such a cipher, but this particular antique dealer hasn't won a haggle with the author for a long time, and he won't until he reads this book. As soon as he changes his cipher, we will go after him again.

14. How to Make Ciphers More Difficult to Solve

In the American Civil War, thousands of Confederate soldiers died because the Union cryptographers were able to read some of their vital messages. This is really surprising, since the Confederate Army used an elaborate system of substitution ciphers known as "double-key" or "Vigenère." Methods for solving such ciphers had not yet been published in English. Twenty years earlier, Edgar Allan Poe had simply refused to believe that they could be solved at all.

The Confederates ran into trouble with their ciphers during the Vicksburg campaign. To make certain that their own commanders would be able to read their messages, they retained plain English words in enciphered texts and failed to divide the enciphered portions into five or ten-letter groups.

On the other hand, the Union Army employed word transpositions that completely baffled Southern cipher experts. The far-reaching Confederate cavalry often captured Union messages, and sometimes even the keys, but the Yankees switched keys so often, that the Southern cryptographers were utterly confused. The Confederate government even went so far as to publish intercepted Union messages in newspapers, offering rewards to anyone who could break them, but the rewards were never claimed.

The ciphers themselves were the same sort that James II's experts had broken nearly two hundred years before. (See Chapter 2.) The Union messages could have been broken easily, but they were not. More and more Confederate soldiers died because of bad secret writing.

Southern spies used even more amateurish ciphers than did the Confederate Army. They used simple substitution ciphers, which any clever schoolboy should have been able to read. As a consequence, neither the ciphers nor the spies lasted very long. By cracking one of these ciphers, the Yankees broke up a very important spy ring in New York. They foiled the shipment of smuggled arms via Nova Scotia and captured a set of printing plates that a New York engraver with Southern sympathies had made for reproducing Confederate money. Without the expertly-engraved plates, the Confederate Treasury quickly was forced to make its own. By the end of the Civil War, counterfeit Confederate money could be recognized because the engraving was better than the real thing.

Any system in which the normal length of the words serves as a clue for cipher-breakers is inherently weak. For this reason, almost all good secret writing is transmitted with the cipher text divided into groups of five letters each. Moreover, the receiver can tell if a letter has been omitted. De Rohan's message in Chapter 12 could have been solved by letter frequency and combinations without the word breaks, but they simplified the cryptanalytic process.

Though it would hardly fool a first-rate cipher-cracker, a simple system of reversed writing becomes much more confusing if it is combined with the five-letter group patterns. Our eyes have been trained to read single words. WONTI DAERU OYNAC looks much more difficult than WON TI DAER UOY NAC.

In the early years of the twentieth century, when the British were fighting the Boers in South Africa, British officers, who had no adequate ciphers, sometimes confused their enemies by writing their messages with Greek letters in lieu of the Roman alphabet. Since nearly all of the English had studied Greek, and few of the Boers had, the system worked except in telegraphic communication.

At this time, a new type of substitution, called the Playfair Cipher, was introduced by the British Army. It proved so effective, that it continued in use as the standard field cipher until World War I. This system involves ciphering *pairs of letters* instead of single letters. It is sometimes called a "bigram substitution." Earlier bigram substitutions involved the use of checkerboard patterns of letters in combinations of four or two squares. The British Playfair cipher used a single square. The key word could be memorized so easily that nothing had to be written down and retained.

How does the Playfair work? Using a key word, such as CAPETOWN, the cryptographer sets up an alphabetic sequence in a square. (See FIG. 14.) First, the letters of the key are used; then the remaining letters of the alphabet that are left are written in order. A five-by-five square like the one illustrated is the usual arrangement. Since this square has only twenty-five spaces, and there are twenty-six letters in the alphabet, two letters (usually I and J) share one space. The letters of the message are divided into pairs. Any double letters that fall together must be separated by adding an extra meaningless letter in between.

Let us assume that a message begins with the word ISSUES. The word is split up as IS SU ES. The word MISSION, however, comes out MI SX SI ON. The encipherer is then ready to refer to the square.

When the pair of letters to be enciphered appear in the same row, the pair to their right becomes their cipher equiva-

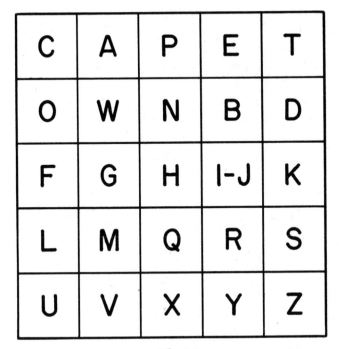

FIG. 14. *Playfair square*

lent (ON equals WB); when they are in the same column, the pair below are used (ER equals BY, CU equals OC, *et cetera*); when they are in neither the same column nor the same row, you use the pair at opposite corners of the rectangle of which the letters form the diagonal. (TH equals PK).

The message HELP IS ON THE WAY is enciphered,

Plain: HE LP IS ON TH EW AY
Cipher: JP QC KR WB PK AB EV

In proper form, the message reads, JPQCK RWBPK ABEVN. The final N is a meaningless letter, or "null," added to complete the final group.

The skillful use of nulls helps to confuse cryptanalysts. They are added to a message in order to facilitate encipherment, to upset frequency counts, and to separate combinations that enemy cipher experts have come to expect.

In Chapter 4 we learned that if a transposition cipher is to fill its "box," nulls sometimes must be added. The best null letters for a transposition are the ones that commonly appear in plain language. A string of Xs at the end of the box might stand out from the text like a sore thumb, thus revealing clues as to the size of the box and the pattern of transposition.

For this reason, E, T, O, A, and N are obvious choices for nulls in transposition ciphers. Instead of placing as many as are needed at the end of the message, a good cryptographer will scatter them through the message, often in places where natural breaks in the meaning suggest that punctuation has been omitted. It is of utmost importance that the nulls in transposition should not be used in any way that might alter the sense of the message. To add NT after the word COULD might prove disastrous.

A good code book may contain a number of null groups to be sprinkled through messages. Code nulls are especially valuable for breaking up phrases that might otherwise appear repetitious.

In substitution ciphers, nulls may be added to fill out the final group to five letters, though again it may be wiser to insert them before the end of the message. In order to disguise letter frequencies, some ciphers specify X as a null between each pair of words.* This makes X the highest frequency letter in the message, occurring more often than E. This practice reveals word lengths, the very breaks that the five-letter system is designed to disguise.

* Some Xs do not happen at word breaks but are intrinsic parts of words.

A safer policy is to use nulls at random. If each letter of the alphabet is written on a piece of paper, and the pieces are then juggled and drawn out of a hat, the nulls can be used to best effect. A mathematical computation enables the sender to change the proportions of the letters in the hat so that all the letters in the final message will appear with the same frequency.

The weakest parts of any secret message—code or cipher— are the beginning and the end. Many messages have headings, indicating place and time; others, particularly diplomatic messages, often start out with set expressions, such as "Referring to your Cablegram No.— . . ." For this reason, code clerks are sometimes instructed to begin all messages with a few words that have nothing to do with the body of the message, or to begin in the middle of the message, so that the beginning and end will be buried in the text.

This kind of padding caused trouble for the Americans in the great battle for Leyte Gulf. On October 29, 1944, Admiral William F. Halsey led the Third Fleet northward from his position east of Luzon to attack Japanese carrier forces. Meanwhile, enemy battleships, which had previously turned back under heavy assault, reversed course and surprised the American Seventh Fleet off the Island of Samar. Headquarters at Pearl Harbor radioed urgently to inquire as to the whereabouts of Halsey's Task Force 34.

In the heat of battle, the communications officer kept the null phrase THE WHOLE WORLD WANTS TO KNOW at the beginning of the message WHERE IS TASK FORCE THIRTY-FOUR? A simple question sounded like a stinging rebuke.

Admiral Halsey already had inflicted heavy damage on the Japanese carriers, but instead of closing in to destroy the whole northern enemy fleet as he had planned, he broke off the engagement and hastened south. He arrived off Samar too late—the Japanese battleships had retired through San Bernardino Strait.

Great care obviously must be taken that nulls do not distort a message. Nevertheless, nulls are valuable aids to cipher security. Sometimes a message can contain more nulls than text. The perforated grill mentioned in Chapter 4 is actually a method of using many nulls. The words of the cover letter, minus the message, are all nulls.

A message can be concealed by nulls alone. In the cryptogram CHGLI ZOZBL MNPHO RZVNV CZNRE BLGRY MAVNO PEZZU, every fifth letter gives the meaning. All the other letters are nulls. This is comparable in effect to a simple grill. It has two great disadvantages: it offers almost no security, and the length of the plain message is increased by 400 per cent. Reversing such a message would increase its security considerably.

Simple substitution can be attacked successfully on the basis of letter frequencies, pairs of letters, and pattern words. Nulls provide some security, especially when carefully used. Another way of safeguarding messages is to use "variants," that is, more than one symbol may be used to represent a single letter. It is possible to use several symbols for E, such as !, #, or $. This cuts down the frequency of any one symbol and confuses anyone who tries to read the message.

The trouble with using such marks as $ and # is the near impossibility of setting up a satisfactory deciphering alphabet with them. One cannot place such signs in alphabetic order, or apply key words to them. Since # and $ cannot be transmitted by radio or cable except by writing them out, they are useless for military and diplomatic correspondence.

Variant letters cause a new complication. Since it is impossible for both D and M to stand for E without running out of letters before the cipher alphabet is complete, *two*

			2	3	4	5	6	7	8	9	1
1	4	7	A	D	G	J	M	P	S	V	Y
2	5	8	B	E	H	K	N	Q	T	W	Z
3	6	9	C	F	I	L	O	R	U	X	

FIG. 15

letter combinations must be used to stand for each single letter of the plain text. This doubles the length of the cryptogram.

It is possible to work out a fairly satisfactory substitution with variants based on numbers. The letter A in FIG. 15 may be 12 on its first appearance, 42 on its second, and 72 on its third. The word NOON can be enciphered three times three times three times three, or eighty-one different ways (26-36-36-26, 56-36-36-26, *et cetera*). This enciphering system is easy to use and remember.

A better use of variants assigns the most commonly-used letters (E, T, O, A, N, I, R, S, H, *et cetera*) the greatest number of different equivalents. With this system (See FIG. 16), NOON can be written 1296 different ways (45-73-93-65, 55-73-93-65, *et cetera*).

The number of cipher equivalents can be increased greatly if letters in pairs are used instead of pairs of numbers to designate a single letter. (See FIG. 17.) There are twenty-six letters,

						1	2	3	4	5	6	7	8	9
4	5	6	7	8	9	E	T	O	A	N	I	R	S	H
				2	3	D	L	C	W	U	M	F	Y	G
					1	P	B	V	K	X	Q	J	Z	

FIG. 16

```
                          A
                          B  E  H  K  N  Q  T
                          C  F  I  L  O  R  U  W  Y
                          D  G  J  M  P  S  V  X  Z
A B C D E F G H I J K │E│T│O│A│N│I│R│S│H│
    L M N O P Q R S T │D│L│C│W│U│M│F│Y│G│
        U V W X Y Z P │P│B│V│K│X│Q│J│Z│
```

FIG. 17

but only ten numbers. There are 100 possible number pairs, if zero is included, from 00 to 99, and 676 letter pairs from AA to ZZ. In FIG 17, there are forty-four possible forms for E instead of the six of the previous rectangle. The variants are AA, AB, AC, AD, BA . . . KD. This cipher could be made more secure by scrambling the order of the cipher equivalents outside the rectangle. In FIG. 17, they are shown in normal alphabetical sequence. Using this system, one can write the word NOON 1,185,921 different ways.

The weakness of variant systems lies in their application. It has been said that the most unreliable part of a car is the nut that holds the steering wheel; the most unreliable part of a cipher system is usually the crytographer who uses it.

Unless the variant values are chosen by some carefully prepared plan, anyone using such a system in haste is likely to employ the same value for E over and over, neglecting the other forty-three possibilities. Although there are many equivalents for E, any one of them always means E. Unless a method is used that provides shifting variants, whereby X might mean E at one point, and T at another, the system itself is no more than simple substitution with a few frills.

15. Polyalphabetic Substitution

WHAT is a perfect cipher? Is it possible to work out a simple method of substitution whereby letter frequencies are disguised, the key can be reconstructed easily from memory, and the enciphered message is no longer than the plain text?

Apparently, no one in northern Europe knew how to accomplish this until 1586, when a brilliant French nobleman, Blaise de Vigenère, published a book in which he described just such a system. If the beautiful Mary, Queen of Scots, had studied a copy of Vigenère's book, her head might have remained on her shoulders.

Although Vigenère drew on the work of the Italian cryptographers Alberti and da Porta, his invention was so simple and so workable, that his name is often used to signify any "double key substitution" or polyalphabetic" system. (Polyalphabetic means "having many alphabets.")

The tableau, or grid, or alphabet square of Vigenère is shown in FIG. 18. Every alphabet is advanced one letter ahead of the one above it.

VIGENÈRE TABLEAU

ABCDEF GHI J KLMNOPQRS TUVWXYZ

1	A	a b c d e f g h i j k l mn o p q r s t u v w x y z
2	B	b c d e f g h i j k l mn o p q r s t u v wx y z a
3	C	c d e f g h i j k l mn o p q r s t u v wx y z a b
4	D	d e f g h i j k l mn o p q r s t u v wx y z a b c
5	E	e f g h i j k l mn o p q r s t u v wx y z a b c d
6	F	f g h i j k l mn o p q r s t u v wx y z a b c d e
7	G	g h i j k l mn o p q r s t u v wx y z a b c d e f
8	H	h i j k l mn o p q r s t u v wx y z a b c d e f g
9	I	i j k l mn o p q r s t u v wx y z a b c d e f g h
10	J	j k l mn o p q r s t u v wx y z a b c d e f g h i
11	K	k l mn o p q r s t u v wx y z a b c d e f g h i j
12	L	l mn o p q r s t u v wx y z a b c d e f g h i j k
13	M	mn o p q r s t u v wx y z a b c d e f g h i j k l
14	N	n o p q r s t u v wx y z a b c d e f g h i j k l m
15	O	o p q r s t u v wx y z a b c d e f g h i j k l mn
16	P	p q r s t u v wx y z a b c d e f g h i j k l mn o
17	Q	q r s t u v wx y z a b c d e f g h i j k l mn o p
18	R	r s t u v wx y z a b c d e f g h i j k l mn o p q
19	S	s t u v wx y z a b c d e f g h i j k l mn o p q r
20	T	t u v wx y z a b c d e f g h i j k l mn o p q r s
21	U	u v wx y z a b c d e f g h i j k l mn o p q r s t
22	V	v wx y z a b c d e f g h i j k l mn o p q r s t u
23	W	wx y z a b c d e f g h i j k l mn o p q r s t u v
24	X	x y z a b c d e f g h i j k l mn o p q r s t u v w
25	Y	y z a b c d e f g h i j k l mn o p q r s t u v wx
26	Z	z a b c d e f g h i j k l mn o p q r s t u v wx y

FIG. 18

The ordinary alphabet running across the top is the plain-text alphabet. Down the left-hand side, the alphabets are numbered. Inside the square are the twenty-six cipher alphabets, each one shifted one place to the left from the one above it.

The simplest way to use this square is to employ the cipher alphabets in order, using the first row alphabet line (key equals A) for the first letter of the message, the second alphabet (key equals B) for the second letter, and so forth, until twenty-six letters have been enciphered in the twenty-six alphabets. Then the process is repeated until the message is completed.

For example, YOU MUST COME HERE AT ONE is enciphered in the following manner: the cryptographer locates each letter of the message in the top, or plain, row and looks down the column under that letter for the cipher equivalent. Of course, the Y in the first alphabet would still be Y. The O in the second alphabet is P. The U in the third alphabet is W.

Key number
of alphabet: 1 2 3   4 5 6 7   8 9 10 11   12 13 14 15   16 17   18 19 20
Plain message: YOU MUST COM E   H E R E   A T   O N E
Cipher: YPW PYXZ JWVO   S Q E S   P J   F F X

The message is then written in five-letter groups: YPWPY XZJWV OSQES PJFFX. The letter E appears four times in the message, and in the cipher text, it has four different values —O, Q, S, and X. P appears three times in the cipher, and it has three different meanings. The letter frequencies have been successfully disguised, and the cipher is no longer than the original message.

Vigenère was too smart to think that anyone should use his

alphabets in order. As we will see later, a system such as his can be cracked by simply running down the alphabet. The conventional Vigenère system provides for a key to determine exactly which of the twenty-six alphabets is to be used for each letter as it crops up. If the key word for the message is LOVE, the first letter of the message is enciphered from the L line, the twelfth alphabet from the top; the second letter is enciphered from the O, or fifteenth line; the third from the V, or twenty-second line, and the fourth from the E, or fifth line. The process is then repeated indefinitely with those four alphabets.

It is customary to write the key above the letters of the message in order to avoid any confusion as to which key letter controls which letter of the message. To encipher Y with the key letter L, the cryptographer places a ruler across the square line 12 (the L line) and looks down the Y column. The letter above the ruler is J, and J is the cipher equivalent of Y controlled by the key letter L. The message is thus enciphered:

LOV	ELOV	ELOV	ELOV	EL	OVE	Key*
YOU	MUST	COME	HERE	AT	ONE	Plain message
JCP	QFGO	GZAZ	LPFZ	EE	CII	Cipher

FCPQF GOGZA ZLPFZ EECII is the final form, in five-letter groups.

Note that the same key letter, V, has been used twice to encipher the same plain letter, E, giving the same cipher letter, Z. Yet in this short message, the frequencies have been disguised effectively.

* The key determines which alphabet is to be used. This may sound hopelessly complicated, but, with a little practice, you can move swiftly. Most cryptographers prefer to encipher immediately all the letters controlled by a single key letter before resetting the ruler for the next letter.

A longer key word, such as WASHINGTON, produces a wider variety of cipher alphabets and a longer "period" or "cycle" before repetition is necessary. In general, the longer the key word is, and the greater the number of cipher alphabets used, the more secure the resulting message will be. A key phrase or sentence may be used rather than a single word. Since it is dangerous to keep written keys on hand, cryptographers often choose a well-known quotation or proverb. The Lord's Prayer has been a favorite Vigenère key. Anything so well-known has an obvious weakness—it is possible that an enemy might guess its identity.

Deciphering a Vigenère message involves reversing the entire enciphering process. When you use graphite or ink of different colors for the key, you avoid confusion with the cipher message—it is altogether too easy to confuse a cipher letter with a key letter, or vice versa.

Perhaps because Vigenère was also an alchemist, an astrologer, and a dabbler in the occult, his cipher did not come into wide use for a century and a half. The rest of his book was so offbeat and weird, that almost no one recognized the excellent cryptography amid the mass of mystic lore it contained. Eventually, the Germans (before the French or English) capitalized on the potential of polyalphabetic substitution.

Battles have been won or lost, plots have succeeded or failed, and great men and women have lived or died through their ability or inability to read secret messages. By an ironic twist, one ruler apparently accomplished his most cherished ambitions through the misreading of a cipher. Such a mistake might have ruined an unluckier monarch, but this one actually benefitted from careless secret writing.

In the early eighteenth century, the Duke of Brandenburg, the Elector Frederick III, hoped to be recognized as King of Prussia. To accomplish this, he needed the support of the Holy

Roman Emperor, who was not at all eager to see Prussia become a kingdom. Frederick's ambassador at the Emperor's court wrote him a cipher message, urging that he lay his case before the Emperor.

In the figure cipher that he used, 110 denoted the Emperor, but the message was written in haste, and the final O was mistaken for a 6. Now, 116 meant a certain Jesuit priest, Father Wolf, who was confessor to the Emperor's ambassador in Berlin. Frederick III may have been somewhat surprised at this advice, but he immediately acted upon it. He wrote a letter in his own hand to the Jesuit presenting his case and asking for support. If the Duke was surprised at his emissary's advice, the priest was overwhelmed—and flattered—that the Duke should seek his help. He wrote to the Emperor's confessor and the head of his order, urging them both to back Frederick's plan. With the Emperor's consent, the Duke was soon crowned King—because he had misread a single number. That was the first step in the creation of the mighty German Empire, which the Hohenzollerns ruled until World War I.

It is much easier to make fatal mistakes than lucky ones with cipher messages. It was too easy to make mistakes with a Vigenère cipher, but the system was basically so sound that it was bound to be improved upon. Instead of using the cumbersome tableau or alphabet square, cryptographers found that they could obtain identical results by using strips of stiff paper. (See PHOTO 4.)

In its simplest form, this method provides that the first strip should contain a single plain alphabet, while the second has two alphabets, one written immediately following the other. The second strip gives the cipher equivalents. Instead of looking down the left-hand column of the square for his key row, the cryptographer simply places the A of the plain strip directly over the key letter in the cipher strip. The strips are then

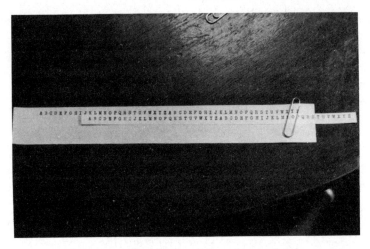

PHOTO 4. *Two paper strips are used for polyalphabetic substitution*

aligned after the manner of the corresponding rows on the Vigenère table, without the other twenty-five lines to confuse the eye. The paper clip in PHOTO 4 holds the strips together so that the cipher strip (bottom) can be manipulated easily.

A more durable and convenient device can be made of heavy paper or cardboard. (See PHOTO 5.) Often the alphabets are mounted on a slide rule in such a way that two alphabets are standard and one in reversed order, can slide against a third. It also provides numerical equivalents. The type shown in PHOTO 6 is known as a St. Cyr slide, in honor of the West Point of France, where military cryptographers have been using such slides since 1880. If a message is enciphered with the identical key on both the Vigenère tableau and the St. Cyr slide, the same cipher message will result.

There is a third device, the cipher wheel, which will produce results identical with those of the slide and the square, and which is perhaps even easier to use. In this simple mechani-

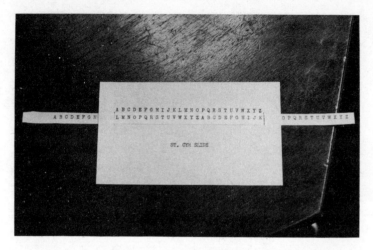

PHOTO 5. *A more convenient St. Cyr slide is used for polyalphabetic substitution*

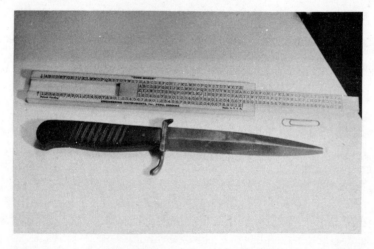

PHOTO 6. *A St. Cyr type of ruler. The knife is of the black, non-glinting variety—the "Fairburne" knife, commonly used in espionage work.*

134

PHOTO 7. *The Cipher Wheel, a St. Cyr Slide is designed in a circle for greater convenience. The object to the right is a tiny gun, commonly referred to in the OSS as an "assassination stick."*

Note that the alphabets of the cipher wheel are reciprocal. K is P, and P is K. B is Y, and Y is B. No matter where the wheel is set, its alphabets are always reciprocal. This one feature eliminates most of the errors that are usually made in polyalphabetic substitution.

Cipher wheels were used as standard communications equipment in the United States Army until well into the twentieth century.

cal device, the alphabet, instead of being on strips, appears in circular form on two disks. (See PHOTO 7, in which a reversed alphabet slides against a standard one.) The cipher wheel is much harder to make than the St. Cyr slide. It is easy to measure off equal spaces for twenty-six letters on a strip of paper, or simply to cut off as much graph paper as you require. It is much more difficult to make twenty-six equal divisions on the

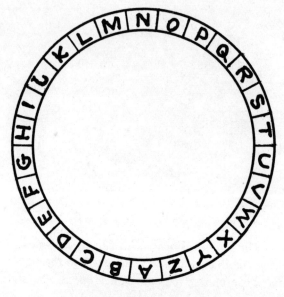

FIG. 19

circumference of a circle, and be certain that each division equals 10.38 degrees. For this reason, we have included two concentric circles already divided. (See FIGS. 19 and 19A.)

These may be cut out, marked with any arrangement of alphabets desired, and mounted on cardboard, or on the tops of tin cans. The larger circle fits a seven-ounce (tuna fish) can, and the smaller one a No. 2 (vegetable) can. A drawing pin may be used to attach disks mounted on cardboard. A small sharp nail may be hammered through the can tops, to fasten them to a piece of wood. Great care should be taken to make certain that the pin or nail passes through the exact center of the disks without bending them.

All the Vigenère-type ciphers demonstrated up to this point use the standard alphabetic sequence of ABCDE . . . and its

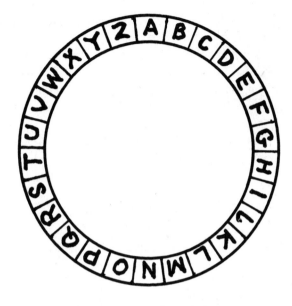

FIG. 19A

reversed form, ZYXWV. Cryptographers can make much safer ciphers. The alphabet may be jumbled with a key word, like the sequences show in Chapters 12 and 14. The term "double-key substitution" refers to the type that uses both a mixed alphabet and an enciphering key.

Whether you use a wheel, slide, or square, the Vigenère is still the same basic cipher system. With word divisions destroyed and letter frequencies suppressed, it might seem to be the ideal cipher, as for many years it was thought to be. The eighteenth-century French writer, Voltaire, stated flatly that anyone who claimed to be able to break such a cipher was a liar.

Edgar Allan Poe, whose ability to solve simple substitutions dazzled most Americans of his time, seems to have had a blind faith in polyalphabetic ciphers. He challenged the readers of *Alexander's Weekly* to send cipher messages to him, claiming that he could solve them all—provided that they did not use a single symbol for more than one letter and that the symbols appeared in normal order. Letters with cipher messages poured in, and Poe, according to his own account, could read them all, even those in foreign languages.

Then in the July, 1841, issue of *Graham's Magazine*, Poe offered another challenge. He presented a cipher that he claimed no one could break. The message used several alphabets, one for each sentence, and involved arbitrary symbols for certain words and syllables. For all his interest in ciphers, Poe seems to have had an incomplete understanding of all the possibilities of Vigenère substitution. One of *Graham's* readers, Richard Bolton, of Pontotoc, Mississippi, solved Poe's "impossible" message.

Poe was flabbergasted. Although he wrote a letter of congratulation to Bolton, he simply refused to believe the evidence before his eyes. Poe claimed that Bolton must have seen the solution, which was published in a later issue. Bolton insisted that he had not.

16. How to Fracture "Poly"

IN a quiet house in the District of Columbia live Mr. and Mrs. William F. Friedman, who know more about cryptography than anyone else in the United States, or perhaps in the world. One of the souvenirs ornamenting their home is a Wheatstone Cryptograph, or self-advancing cipher wheel. It is made of gold. (See FIG. 20.)

Until World War I, the British Army used as its standard field cipher the Playfair, that neat and usable form of bigram substitution described in Chapter 14. In time, the Germans developed such a knack for solving Playfairs that the Allied governments began to look around for a system to replace it.

The Playfair cipher was not the invention of Lord Cyril Playfair—he was merely the wise official who sensed its usefulness and promoted its employment. The cipher itself was worked out by a celebrated physicist, Sir Charles Wheatstone, who made a hobby of cryptography.

During World War I, it occurred to someone in the British War Office that since Sir Charles had invented the brilliant but wornout Playfair, he might have kept a record of other intriguing theories and inventions. Wheatstone had died in 1875, but in his papers, British authorities found a description of a relatively simple and characteristically unique cipher

FIG. 20. *The Wheatstone Cryptograph. This self-advancing cipher wheel advances one letter automatically for each revolution of the inner disk.*

wheel. (See FIG. 20.) This device has since become known as the Wheatstone Cryptograph.

The outer disk has room for a twenty-six-letter alphabet plus a blank space. The inner disk contains twenty-six spaces for a conventional alphabet. Mixed or jumbled alphabets may be used on both disks. Like the hands of a clock, the two circles are so geared that the alignment of the two disks changes for each letter of the message.

Was this the new field cipher the War Office had been seeking? Before putting it into production for widespread military use, the government wisely made arrangements for testing its security. Mixed alphabets, prepared on the basis of two key words, were used to encipher a set of test messages. The messages, together with the key for one of the disks, were forwarded to testing agencies, including the Riverbank Laboratories of Geneva, Illinois. It must always be assumed that a cipher device will be captured from an army unit in the field and that only one of the keys might be changed before further messages are sent.

The Riverbank Laboratories were the project of a colorful character known as Colonel George Fabyan. The military title was honorary, as Fabyan was the Illinois equivalent of a Kentucky Colonel. He had made a large fortune, which he invested in research and experimentation in a wide variety of fields, from agriculture to cryptography. When asked what was raised on his experimental farms, Colonel Fabyan replied, "We raise hell."

The Riverbank Laboratories published some of the most useful frequency tables and solution manuals available outside of the strictly classified documents prepared "for official use only" by government cryptographers. When Colonel Fabyan received the Wheatstone Cryptograph test messages, he was impressed. However, he wanted the opinion of one of his best cipher brains, Bill Friedman. Though he had taken his college degree in agriculture, this young man had shown an uncanny skill with all sorts of cryptographic problems. Colonel Fabyan asked Friedman what he thought of the Wheatstone proposition.

"No good," was Friedman's reply.

"Why not?" the Colonel wanted to know. Since he was deeply engrossed with other problems, Friedman was not eager to undertake a demonstration, but the Colonel reminded him that he was in the habit of receiving a rectangle of paper each month with the Fabyan signature in the lower right-hand corner, and insisted that he take on the assignment.

Friedman looked at the messages and at the one key word, CIPHER. He then approached another of Fabyan's employees, Miss Elizabeth Smith, a young lady who had been working with Mrs. Gallup on the alleged cipher in the First Folio edition of Shakespeare's plays.

Friedman said to Miss Smith, "Please close your eyes and make your mind a blank. I want you to tell me the first word that comes into your mind when I say a word to you. The word is—'cipher'."

"Machine," Miss Smith replied.

Friedman set up the blank disk of the Wheatstone Cryptograph with a sequence based on the key word MACHINE. A million-to-one chance—but he read off the test messages with it.

This is a startling example of the part that intuition can play in breaking cipher messages. Needless to say, the Allies looked elsewhere for new field ciphers. If Miss Smith could make such an incredible guess, perhaps the German cryptanalysts might be as lucky.

Miss Smith eventually became Mrs. Friedman, and the government of the United States acquired the services of the talented couple. For many years, Colonel William F. Friedman was the chief cryptanalyst of the War Department, while Mrs. Friedman held a similar position with the Secret Service.

There is no way of assessing this couple's value to their country. Whatever cipher machines Mr. Friedman invented for the American Army could not be patented, since all patents must be accompanied by descriptions and working models, and Patent Office records are available to anyone, including foreign agents. In 1956, however, the Congress voted the sum of $100,000 to Mr. Friedman in partial restitution for the royalties he could not collect on machines that could not be patented.

With the twenty-six standard alphabets of the Vigenère square used in order, a polyalphabetic cipher resembles the

Julius Caesar variety—with an added dimension. It can be solved in a similar manner, but with an important difference. If a cryptanalyst were to encounter YPWPY XZJWV OSQES PJFFX, he would first satisfy himself that it was not transposition or a simple substitution. Then he would run down the alphabet.

```
Y P WP Y X Z J W V O S Q E S P J F F X
Z Q X Q Z Y A K X W P T R F T Q K G G Y
A R Y R A Z B L Y X Q U S G U R L H H Z
B S Z S B A C M Z Y R V T H V S MI I A
C T A T C B D N A Z S W U I W T N J J B
D U B U D C E O B A T X V J X U O K K C
E V C V E D F P C B U Y W K Y V P L L D
F W D W F E G Q D C V Z X L Z W Q M M E
G X E X G F H R E D W A Y M A X R N N
H Y F Y H G I S F E X B Z N B Y S O
I Z G Z I H J T G F Y C A O C Z T
J A H A J I K U H G Z D B P D A
K B I B K J L V I H A E C Q E
L C J C L K M W J I B F D R
MD K D M L N X K J C G E
N E L E N M O Y L K D H
O F MF O N P Z ML E
P G N G P O Q A N M
Q H O H Q P R B O
R I P I R Q S C
S J Q J S R T
T K R K T S
U L S L U
V M T M
W N U
X O
Y
```

Instead of appearing on a line, as the Caesar Cipher does, the original message appears in a diagonal. The diagonal that makes sense is the message: YOU MUST COME HERE AT ONE.

As soon as a key word is introduced to control the order in which the alphabets are used, the solution becomes enormously tougher.

In 1863, a brilliant Prussian staff officer, Major Kasiski, published a book on cryptography showing an elegant method of solving the enigma. The first step in his method is to discover all repetitions. Practically every message contains some repeated combinations, sometimes several words in length. While these are less apparent in Vigenère ciphers than in simple substitutions, sooner or later, the same phase of the keying cycle will control the same letter combinations in the plain text. This means that the cipher text will eventually betray itself through occasional repetitions.

Kasiski showed that it was possible to figure out the length of the key word by counting the number of letters between each pair of repeated sequences. The number is almost bound to be a multiple of the number of letters in the key word. The different alphabets can then be sorted into homogeneous groups, and, with a lot of perseverance and a little luck, the meaning can be worked out on the basis of letter frequencies.

A French cryptographer, Kerkhoffs, found a short cut by working backward through the key. He noted that if, for example, F in one alphabet is identified as O of the plain text, the alphabet strips indicate that A of the plain line equals R on the cipher line. This means that R is the key letter in control. Knowing one or two letters of the key often enables the cryptanalyst to guess the whole key word or sentence, unless the alphabets are mixed. This cracks the message immediately.

Kerkhoffs' discovery was used by Bazeries, one of the greatest cryptanalysts of all time, to save the Third Republic of France from a Royalist plot that would have destroyed it. By the year 1899, the democratic government of France was teetering on the brink of disaster. Military and financial scandals had weakened the confidence of many French people in the Republic. A hard core of determined Royalists sought to convince them that the salvation of France lay in the over-throw of democracy and the restoration of the monarchy.

A leader of this movement was Paul Déroulède, whose patriotic poems and plays enjoyed an enthusiastic audience. He founded a League of Patriots, which he tried to forge into a weapon for subverting the government. Many loyal Frenchmen left the League when they saw in what direction Déroulède was leading them. The die-hard members went underground.

Eventually, the police got their hands on a number of cipher messages used by Déroulède and his associates. The material was turned over to the Black Chamber, the crack cryptanalytic agency that the French Army had developed. There the brilliant Commandant Bazeries studied the mes-sages. Though they were written in figures rather than letters, Bazeries recognized in them a variant of the Vigenère system. He had little enough to go on, and while he could have solved them in time, perhaps with Kasiski's system, the plot he knew was developing might well have been hatched before the laborious mathematical process could lead to a solution.

Instead, Bazeries decided to use a "probable" word—Déroulède's name—to discover the key. It yielded pure non-sense. He then tried the last name of another known plotter, Thuret, and this yielded a "key" of TDEEDI, from the first six letters of one of the messages—not a real word, but at least a clue. The three final letters EDI, he surmised, could be identified with *Samedi* (Saturday), the day on which the message was written. Using SAMEDI as the key, Bazeries deciphered the first six letters of the message—SECRET. The *ret* of SECRET matched the *ret* of Thuret. By the completely accidental similarity of words, the wrong guess had led to the right answer. The message had been broken.

Its contents revealed that the Royalists were waiting for the perfect moment when the crowds were in the streets, to strike against the government. And as if to provide the conspirators with their opportunity, President Faure of the French Republic died. His timing was perfect. At the great public funeral in Paris on February 23, the mob was ready to listen to Déroulède and his fellow rabble-rousers. But the government had been tipped off by Bazeries, and units of the French Army from points a hundred miles away were rushed in to march in the funeral procession. In the face of this armed display, the crowds failed to respond to the plot. And the Royalists were equally unsuccessful in stirring up mutiny among the fore-warned military units.

Déroulède was arrested and brought to trial, but the government was unwilling to tip its hand and reveal that Bazeries had been the ace in the hole. The poet was acquitted for the lack of evidence and continued to plot against the Republic. He sent new cipher messages that presented new difficulties. No longer was the day of the week used as key. The new key was as long as the messages. Again Bazeries resorted to probable words, and, this time, he discovered that the key was a stanza from a poem by Alfred de Musset. Plotters' minds seem to run in predictable channels: the next day's messages were ciphered with the next stanza of the poem.

The police were prepared to close in on the Royalists when suddenly their messages became unreadable. Bazeries guessed that this time, the cipher strip itself had been changed—no longer was he dealing with a standard alphabet. Never at a loss, the clever cryptanalyst reasoned that although the alphabet had changed, perhaps the key would still be the succeeding stanza from de Musset. Miraculously, his hunch proved correct.

The plotters were tried again, and, this time, the French government was frightened enough to put Bazeries himself on the witness stand. Déroulède and his henchmen were banished from France, and the Third Republic settled down to a quieter existence.

Instead of a poem, the plotters might have used a numerical key. The value of π can be carried out to as many places as a cryptographer requires, but a spy would have to carry a computer around on his back in order to find his key. The square root of two, or three, or five, serves as well. Any fraction can be turned into a decimal by dividing its numerator by its denominator. Six-sevenths is easily committed to memory. Curiously enough, however, all decimal fractions eventually either come out even or else repeat themselves. Thus a fraction produces the same kind of key as a word or phrase, and any message enciphered with one can be attacked by Kasiski's method.

Other variations on the Vigenère system involve changing the length of a repeated key. Kasiski's solution will not work if the key cycle is interrupted at irregular intervals—that is, at the end of each word in the message, or whenever a certain prearranged letter appears in it.

To avoid repeating the key, even in part, cryptographers sometimes use a keying sequence as long as the message to be enciphered. The message can even be used as its own key. The cryptographer primes the pump by enciphering the be-

ginning with a single key letter or a short key word, and proceeds to copy his cipher text, as fast as he produces it, over
the subsequent letters of the plain text:

K	I	W	Q	C	W					Key
Y	O	U	M	U		S	T	C	O	M	E	Plain Message
I	W	Q	C	W						Cipher

This method appears to offer greater security than it actually
possesses. If a cryptanalyst suspects that the message before
him has been produced by such a "cipher auto-key," he need
look no further—the key is already in his hands. From time
to time, it occurs to some amateur cryptographer to use the
plain text of the message, shifted one or more letters to the
right by the priming, as its own key. This system, known as
plain auto-key, sounds perfect. In order to break the message,
one must know the message. The box is locked with the key
inside!

Can such complex ciphers ever be broken? Yes, if there
are enough messages, enough mathematicians, and enough
equipment on hand. From the very fact that some letters appear more commonly than others in any readable key, a competent cryptanalytic team can reduce the mass of enciphered
material by statistical analysis. Neither the message itself,
nor even a book such as the *Encyclopaedia Britannica* can be
the perfect key.

Since repetition of the key provides the cryptanalyst with a
point of attack, the perfect key must never be repeated, no
matter how many messages the correspondents exchange.
Since the letter frequency distributions inherent in any readable key provide another point of attack, the perfect key must
be a meaningless sequence of letters (or numbers). Such a
random key can be obtained by drawing letters from a hat.

(The process for constructing a random key is the same as that described in Chapter 14 for the selection of nulls.)

In this way, two correspondents can make up identical keying strips and communicate with absolute security, destroying pieces of the keying strip as soon as they are used. It is cumbersome to make, duplicate, and carry around such a key, and there is always the danger of capture. A random keying strip has greater security than any code book, but it is just as incriminating to the owner.

On Saturday, January 7, 1961, officers of Scotland Yard's Special Branch arrested a dealer in old books, together with his wife, at their suburban London home. The couple, known as Peter and Helen Kroger, were denied bail for excellent reasons. Scotland Yard had good grounds for believing that they were spies in the service of Soviet Russia.

A few hours might have given the couple an opportunity to destroy what it took days and weeks for the officers to find in their modest bungalow. On the living-room table was a cigarette lighter that looked like any other circular Ronson. The chamber that held the fluid had a false bottom and underneath were tiny documents of enormous significance. There were three microfilmed signal plans, indicating in detail on what days and at what hours clandestine radio communication with Moscow was to take place. Also, in the chamber were two little rolls, as yet unused, of random key pages, and two more rolls, partially used, from which pages had been torn off and destroyed. Undoubtedly, the missing pages had served their purpose by providing keys for messages already transmitted to Moscow. The pads were made of highly inflammable material. If the Krogers had had any warning of their impending arrest, it would have been simple to burn the damning evidence.

Whenever British and American authorities have succeeded

in capturing Russian spy messages, they have been unable to break them. No analysis, however painstaking and inspired, can be accomplished on cryptograms produced by means of non-repeating random keys. Soviet espionage is extraordinarily methodical. The messages that the Krogers sent from London were enciphered in the same way as others intercepted by the FBI in New York. The system is uniform and unassailable. Even if the officers were to capture an exact plain-text copy of a message, together with its enciphered equivalent, there would be no clue to help them attack another cryptogram passing between the same correspondents.

The stark impossibility of cracking a cipher may well stagger the reader's imagination, but he has heard nothing yet. One of the sharpest practices of cryptography is to jam the crypt-analytic facilities of an enemy by transmitting hundreds of messages *that have absolutely no meaning whatsoever.* They are intended to keep the enemy's best cryptanalytic brains and machinery tied up while they try to solve impossible problems. Writing a fake code or cipher message that will consume thousands of enemy man hours is a science in itself. Since completely random texts can be identified as such, the pseudo-cryptograms must contain false clues suggestive of complex cipher systems. By what scientific process can a secret that isn't a secret be made to look like a secret?

17. Intuition in Cryptanalysis

THE cryptanalyst knows that there is one right answer, if only he can find it. Instead of struggling to reveal secrets of nature, or unravel patterns of behavior, the cryptanalyst searches for the secrets of other human beings. Unlike the scientist, philosopher, or economist, who searches for solutions that may not exist, the cryptanalyst knows that the answer he seeks is the only possible answer.

The great cryptanalysts are virtually a breed apart; they are dedicated men and women who work day and night. Breaking ciphers is at once their vocation and their avocation.

In 1943, a young Signal Corps lieutenant, fresh out of Officer Candidate School, was assigned the job of courier, carrying documents back and forth between Army and Navy communications units in Washington. His schedule was such that he arrived each morning to pick up his bundle of top-secret stuff from the Navy outfit at the time when his blue-coated brothers-in-arms were having their coffee break. Actually, a good deal of constructive work was done in bull sessions over the coffee cups and doughnuts, though the Army lieutenant nursed the impression that the Navy was strictly a social con-fab. The men sat back, their feet on their desks, smoking and cracking jokes about their work.

One morning, when the courier entered, he was amazed to see the Navy officers huddled over a table, scribbling furiously. One looked up tensely and inquired, "Hey, Mike, anyone over at G-2 got this yet?" Their "problem" proved to be a con-cealed message in Milton Caniff's comic strip, *Terry and the Pirates*. A character named Flip Corkin, trapped by a Japanese agent in a remote Asiatic village, had been monopolizing all the frames for a week while he tried to tip off his general with a cipher in which the dots of the i's and the crossings of the t's represented the dots and dashes of Morse Code. Flip's cleverly-devised cover letter fooled the spy into letting it pass through.

The cipher looked sound in print. It was relatively unwork-able in practice because the divisions between letters could not be indicated. Except for the comic-strip general, almost no one, Army or Navy, was able to catch on.

Not infrequently, a solution presents itself to the researcher in a dream, or in that half-waking state when his unconscious mind "surfaces." It was thus that Colonel Yardley made the key assumptions that led to the breaking of the Japanese diplomatic code before the Washington Naval Conference. The use of iodine vapor to detect invisible ink is supposed to be another dream revelation.

This day-and-night preoccupation with the same absorbing problem induces a special form of emotional strain on cipher-breakers. They live and breathe their work, and since they are usually obliged never to speak of it except to a handful of co-workers, they are especially vulnerable to mental strain. The value of a cipher's meaning usually declines steadily with each passing hour. Even lesser clerks may feel this pressure. One girl spent her days searching messages for repetitions, and her nights dreaming that she was trying to match grains of sand by the seashore.

Much of the mechanical side of cryptanalysis now can be handled by mechanical means, though no machine can substitute for the mind of a good cryptanalyst. He must work logically and mathematically, but also intuitively. When he has carefully calculated his frequency tables, he must use his imagination to guess the values of a few letters, or to assume probable words, and he must go on guessing, over and over again, rejecting part of his own work, beginning over and retracing his steps. If he is dealing with a cipher rather than a code, he will probably know, and be able to prove, that his solution is correct—a tremendous satisfaction. At last the problem will have been reduced to a system with specific keys.

> The golden guess
> Is morning star to the full round of truth.

One of the most appalling tests ever to confront a cryptanalyst was that presented by the so-called German fractional system in 1918. From the beginning of the war, the German armies had used double-columnar transposition. Difficult as this proved to be (both for the Germans who used it and for the Allied researchers who had to break it for its keys, once they had solved the basic system), it was much easier than the cipher that they sprang before their 1918 offensive.

A fractional cipher is actually a combined substitution and transposition. One form involves the use of a five-square checkerboard, superficially not unlike that of a Playfair. Instead of substituting by pairs of letters, however, the cipher

	1	2	3	4	5
1	F	R	A	C	T
2	I-J	O	N	L	B
3	D	E	G	H	K
4	M	P	Q	S	U
5	Y	W	X	Y	Z

FIG. 21. *Fractional grill*

clerk finds the equivalent of each letter by reading a pair of numerical equivalents, first from the vertical line to the left, then from the horizontal one across the top.

In the following example (See FIG. 21), the alphabet is a mixed one, based on the word FRACTIONAL placed in a five-by-five square. After the word FRACTIONAL has been written in the square horizontally (with I and J combined to provide a total of only twenty-five letters), those letters of the alphabet that are left over are entered in their normal order. The first equivalent of F is 11 (1 from the vertical column corresponding to it, and 1 from the horizontal row). The equivalent of R is 12, *et cetera.* In encipherment, however, the digit pairs are written as $\frac{1}{1}$ and $\frac{1}{2}$. The message WILL BE READY TO GO becomes,

```
W I L L   B E   R E A D Y   T O   G O
5 2 2 2   2 3   1 3 1 3 5   1 2   3 2
2 1 4 4   5 2   2 2 3 1 4   5 2   3 2
```

When put into five-letter groups, this may be read off as

52222 31313 51232
21445 22231 45232

More often than not the text is reciphered by reading it backwards into the same square. The equivalent for 52 is W and that of 22 is O. The message can be WONAA VNOCU ONCWE, and the final cipher message has the same number of letters as the clear original.

As if this nightmare were not complicated enough, the digits from 6 through 0, which are, of course, not needed, can be used as variants or as nulls to further confuse things. Instead of using the square, you can accomplish the final recipherment by arbitrarily substituting letters for each of the integers in the pairs of digits. In the example above, where W is 52, this could then become EB (the fifth and second letters in the alphabet). Of course, any other method of choosing the letters would work as well.

In 1918, the Germans chose to use the ten letters with the most distinctive pattern in Morse Code, thus minimizing the danger of garbles in transmission. The cipher message produced in this way, unlike that illustrated in FIG. 21, has the disadvantage of being exactly twice as long as the original text.

Although using such a cipher under battle conditions put

a tremendous strain on the German signalmen, the Allies were faced with the appalling problem of trying to break this monstrosity. A celebrated French cryptanalyst, Georges Painvain, attempted this seeming impossibility. Working under the terrible pressure of the final German assault, he sweated over the problem day and night. Some weeks later, he emerged with the solution—and a nervous breakdown.

Only a group of dedicated experts can analyze modern ciphers. They need all the help that they can get from scientific data-processing machines, any scraps of information they can find having to do with the subject matter of the messages and the mental quirks of their opponents, and any cipher sheets or code books that watchful agents can gather for them. Code and cipher experts have been known to hail the pilfering of work sheets or of code books as "practical cryptanalysis." (See Chapter 9.)

It must be apparent that the exact plain text of any message known to have been sent in code or cipher is of tremendous value. In the case of cipher, such a "pony" can reveal the general system in use and the specific keys as well. In the case of code, the pony is less valuable, but it is certainly helpful in determining the meaning of certain code groups.

Deciphered messages must never be kept on file because a spy might photostat them. However, since it is often necessary to have the substance of the messages on hand for reference or forwarding, they can be carefully paraphrased. The original form then can be destroyed.

A regular method is used in paraphrasing to alter the sequence of paragraphs, sentences, and word order. Synonyms are employed to take the place of words with equivalent meanings. Thus WE WILL BE READY TO ATTACK AT DAWN might find its way into a file drawer as SUNRISE ASSAULT

BY OUR FORCES PREPARED FOR. The longer the message, the easier paraphrasing becomes.

If there are dangers inherent in keeping the exact texts of messages, there are also dangers, sometimes of a psychological sort, in paraphrasing. The tensions that often build up between people who must work at great distances from one another are usually overcome by diplomatic and tactful communications. In the experience of the OSS, paraphrasing so destroys the nuances of such messages, that it causes a measurable percentage of destructive tension that exists between an agency's officers.

For example, when the message IMPORTANT THAT YOU GO AS SOON AS POSSIBLE TO PARIS hits the desk of a sensitive associate, it might read, OBLIGATORY THAT YOU LEAVE FOR PARIS IMMEDIATELY. The first is a diplomatic request; the second an almost arrogant order.

It is even possible for a radical change of meaning to result from paraphrasing. The original statement MR. SMITH WAS NOT DRUNK LAST SATURDAY, could be filed as, MR. SMITH WAS SOBER ON JULY 18. The rephrasing suggests that after going on a bender for several days, Smith dried out, perhaps preparatory to another binge.

Paraphrasing of deciphered messages is absolutely necessary. The experts are always standing by, with sharp pencils and sharper minds, to match wits with the men who invent and use the ciphers.

18. A Patriot's Code

At 7:55 on the morning of December 7, 1941, the eighty-eight ships of the United States Pacific Fleet were riding at anchor at Pearl Harbor. Suddenly, with no warning at all, the fleet was attacked by a force of over a hundred Japanese torpedo planes, and an undetermined number of midget two-man submarines.

In a few minutes, the United States Pacific Fleet, one of the most formidable naval forces the world had ever seen, was a shambles. The battleships *Arizona, Nevada, Oklahoma, West Virginia,* and *California*—the backbone of United States sea power in the Pacific—were smoking scrap piles. Three destroyers, one mine-layer, and a target ship also were destroyed. The battleships *Maryland, Tennessee,* and *Pennsylvania* and the cruisers *Raleigh, Honolulu,* and *Helena* were badly damaged. The unloading, repairing, and drydock facilities were torn up, and a hundred and seventy-seven United States military airplanes were completely destroyed.

It was one of the most devastating defeats in the history of naval warfare; the Japanese lost only forty-eight airplanes and three midget submarines, and less than one hundred men.

When the news finally leaked out, American public opinion demanded a victim, and the issue swiftly became political. Stories were even going the rounds that President Roosevelt had connived in the destruction of the American Fleet in order to justify America's entrance into the war.

Investigations were started, only to die mysteriously. The American public was baffled, enraged, and eager for information, but even men in high places were unable to obtain all the facts.

It was years before the story came out, and perhaps it can never be told in full. Astonishingly, in a twenty-year cycle, the history of codes and ciphers had repeated itself. After the American Black Chamber had cracked the Japanese ciphers—a feat that led to the defeat of Japan in the Washington Naval Conference—the Japanese were almost hysterically determined to set up code and cipher systems that no one could solve. Yet, despite the enormous work and skill that went into the new Japanese secret communications systems, most of their codes and ciphers eventually were broken by the uncanny skill of the American cryptographers.

Unfortunately, none of the enormous volume of Japanese messages, whose secrets were being unlocked in the United States, mentioned the coming attack on Pearl Harbor until, to quote General George Catlett Marshall, "the last message before December 7th, which did not reach our hands until the following day, December 8th."

Evidently, the message that should have warned of the attack was unscrambled in time, but the frantic cryptographer literally was unable to contact anyone with the authority to act swiftly. Everything at the top level seemed to be closed up for the week end. An hour or two's notice would have permitted the United States Fleet to deploy in the open Pacific, but the notice came too late.

This story could not be disclosed to the American public without also informing the Japanese that the United States had broken their cipher secrets. By the time the presidential campaign came along in 1944, two issues stood out above all others: (1) Should any United States President serve for a fourth term and (2) What were the facts concerning the Pearl Harbor debacle, and why were they being concealed?

New York's Governor Thomas E. Dewey, an accomplished campaigner, plunged into the fight with everything he had. The first issue spoke for itself, but the Pearl Harbor issue became more violent and important each day.

One morning, while Governor Dewey was campaigning in Tulsa, Oklahoma, a man knocked on his door and handed him a letter. On the envelope was the phrase,

TOP SECRET FOR MR. DEWEY'S EYES ONLY.

The courier, a tall, strikingly handsome man, was a full army colonel in civilian clothes, Colonel Carter W. Clark, He had just been flown out from Washington on a bomber. Governor Dewey opened the letter, and found that it was from General Marshall. Its first paragraph was a shocker:

I am writing you without the knowledge of any other person except Admiral King (who concurs) because we are approaching a grave dilemma in the political reactions of Congress regarding Pearl Harbor.

What I have to tell you below is of such a highly secret nature that I feel compelled to ask you either to accept it on the basis of your not communicating its contents to any other person and returning this letter, or not reading any further and returning the letter to the bearer.

Although dying of curiosity, Governor Dewey stopped immediately and handed the letter back to the Colonel with the rest of its contents unread. He pointed out that he did not want to be put in the position of promising not to divulge information that he already might know. He also said that a candidate for the presidency was in no position to make blind promises.

Governor Dewey returned to the East and shortly afterward, the handsome Colonel showed up again with a letter that carried the following instruction on the envelope:

TOP SECRET FOR MR. DEWEY'S EYES ONLY.

Governor Dewey opened the letter and found that its first paragraph had been greatly diluted:

You are bound not to communicate to any other person any portions on which you do not now have or later receive factual knowledge from some other person than myself. . . . You have my word that neither the Secretary of War nor the President has any intimation whatsoever that such a letter has been addressed to you.

This time, seeing that he would be allowed to retain a copy of the letter, Governor Dewey kept on reading:

The most vital evidence in the Pearl Harbor matter consists of our intercepts of the Japanese diplomatic communications. Over a period of years our cryptograph people analyzed the character of the machine the Japanese are using for encoding their diplomatic messages. Based on this, a corresponding machine was built by us which deciphers their messages.

Therefore, we possessed a wealth of information regarding their moves in the Pacific which in turn was furnished the State Department—rather than, as is popularly supposed, the State Department providing us with the information—but which unfortunately made no reference whatever to intentions toward Hawaii until the last message before December 7, which did not reach our hands until the following day, December 8.

Now the point to the present dilemma is that we have gone ahead with this business of deciphering their codes until we possess other codes, German as well as Japanese, but our main basis of information regarding Hitler's intentions in Europe is obtained from Baron Oshima's messages from Berlin reporting his interviews with Hitler and other officials to the Japanese Government. These are still in the codes involved in the Pearl Harbor events.

To explain further the critical nature of this setup which would be wiped out almost in an instant if the least suspicion were aroused regarding it, the Battle of the Coral Sea was based on deciphered messages and therefore our few ships were in the right place at the right time. Further, we were able to concentrate on our limited forces to meet their advances on Midway when otherwise we almost certainly would have been some 3,000 miles out of place.

We had full information of the strength of their forces in that advance and also of the smaller force directed against the Aleutians which finally landed troops on Attu and Kiska.

Operations in the Pacific are largely guided by the information we obtain of Japanese deployments. We know their strength in various garrisons, the rations and other stores continuing available to them, and what is of vast importance, we check their fleet movements and the movements of their convoys.

The heavy losses reported from time to time which they sustain by reason of our submarine action largely results from the fact that we know the sailing dates and the routes of their convoys and can notify our submarines to lie in wait at the proper point.

The current raids by Admiral Halsey's carrier forces on Japanese shipping in Manila Bay and elsewhere were largely based on timing on the known movements of Japanese convoys, two of which were caught, as anticipated, in his destructive attacks.

You will understand from the foregoing the utter tragic consequences if the present political debates regarding Pearl Harbor disclose to the enemy, German or Jap, any suspicion of the vital sources of information we now possess.

The Robert's report on Pearl Harbor had to have withdrawn from it all reference to this highly secret matter, therefore in portions it necessarily appeared incomplete. The same reason which dictated that course is even more important today because our sources have been greatly elaborated.

As a further example of the delicacy of the situation, some of Donovan's people (the OSS), without telling us, instituted a secret search of the Japanese Embassy offices in Portugal. As a result the entire military attaché Japanese code all over the world was changed, and though this occurred over a year ago, we have not yet been able to break the new code and have thus lost this invaluable source of information, particularly regarding the European situation.

A recent speech in Congress by Representative Harness would clearly suggest to the Japanese that we have been reading their codes, though Mr. Harness and the American public would probably not draw any such conclusion.

The conduct of General Eisenhower's campaign and of

all operations in the Pacific are closely related in conception and timing to the information we secretly obtain through these intercepted codes. They contribute greatly to the victory and tremendously to the savings of American lives, both in the conduct of current operations and in looking toward the early termination of the war.

The last paragraph of General Marshall's letter stated,

I am presenting this matter to you, for your secret information, in the hope that you will see your way clear to avoid the tragic results with which we are now threatened in the present political campaign.

Upon reading this letter, Governor Dewey made the only decision a loyal American could have made. He decided to put the interests of the United States above his own political ambition. The Pearl Harbor controversy, which was thought by most of his advisers to be the key to his campaign for the presidency, gradually faded as an issue.

Roosevelt's victory in the 1944 election was astonishingly close. If only one voter in twenty-six had changed his vote from Franklin Roosevelt to Thomas Dewey, because he knew the full facts about Pearl Harbor, Governor Dewey would have been elected President of the United States.

It is highly probable that a continuation of this violent controversy, with its inevitable disclosure that the United States had lost its Pacific Fleet because no one in the administration had been minding the store over the week end, would have changed a lot more votes than one in twenty-six.

When Governor Dewey and General Marshall met at President Roosevelt's funeral, the Governor learned that Roosevelt died without ever having been told the story of the Top-Secret letter that had made him President for the fourth time.

19. The Machine Takes Over

ONE of the great mysteries of all times is the identity of the "Man in the Iron Mask." In 1674, the people of Pignerol, in northern Italy, saw a tall masked man walking the battlements of the French prison under heavy guard. In later years, he was moved to other prisons, and died in the grim Paris fortress of the Bastille. A fellow inmate subsequently recorded that the unknown prisoner had been kept under guard and masked for thirty-one years, and that the mask itself was made of iron.

Many people tried to guess who the man in the mask was. Since the guards always treated him with respect, everyone agreed that he must be a person of high birth and great importance, perhaps a prince. Alexandre Dumas wrote a novel in which the prisoner appeared as a twin brother of King Louis XIV of France. Others suggested he might have been a son of King Charles II of England.

Nearly two centuries after the prisoner died, the mystery took a cryptographic twist. Commandant Bazeries of the Black Chamber was called in to see if he could read certain two-hundred-year-old messages in connection with a military history on which a brother officer was working. No one else had been able to make head or tail of the cipher in which jumbles of numbers had been written. But Bazeries was one of the greatest cryptanalysts ever produced by France, the country that has given us so many of them.

When the messages turned out to be much more difficult than the usual disguised substitution that Bazeries had expected, he suddenly realized that he must be dealing with the Great Cipher of Louis XIV, the unbreakable system that the cryptographic genius Rossignol had invented to protect the secrets of the Sun-King. When Louis XIV had died in 1715, the secret of this famous cipher supposedly had perished with him.

Bazeries analyzed the series of messages and found that it contained 587 number groups in all—too few for a code and too many for a cipher. He came to the conclusion that actually he was attempting to solve a sort of pre-code, a system in which each number group might represent either a syllable or a single letter. Many variants complicated the cipher further. He attacked one group of messages on the basis of this theory, and thus the Great Cipher, which had been the despair of cryptanalysts and historians for over two hundred years, was finally broken.

One of the most interesting Great Cipher messages in the set that Bazeries solved concerned the fate of General Bulonde. Bulonde had angered Louis XIV by disobeying the King's orders. Instead of taking the Italian fort of Coni, the capture of which was vital to the King's plans, Bulonde played the coward and broke off the siege. Louvois, the enraged King's Minister of War, sent orders in the Great Cipher that Bulonde was to be arrested immediately and imprisoned at Pignerol. There he was to be allowed to exercise by walking on the battlements with a "303 309." The groups 303 and 309 appeared nowhere else in the series of messages; there was no clue to their meaning. Bazeries decided that they might signify a mask.

Was the insubordinate and cowardly general really the "Man in the Iron Mask"? It is no reflection on the greatness of Bazeries as a cryptanalyst that a later historical detective showed that Bulonde was alive and free two years after the death of the masked prisoner.

Another of Bazeries' great successes came about in connection with a literary cryptogram. Nineteenth-century writers delighted in presenting cipher messages in their stories and then dazzling their readers with the solution. Poe, Jules Verne, and Conan Doyle featured cryptograms. Honoré de Balzac, one of the great novelists of all time, presented three pages of mysterious secret writing in *La Physiologie du Mariage*, and generations of cryptographers, professional and amateur, could not crack it.

Finally Bazeries proved by carefully-reasoned analysis that Balzac was teasing his readers. The "message" was cleverly-contrived nonsense, with sufficient hints at repetition to look like the real thing.

Bazeries' greatest accomplishment was the invention of a cipher machine that is the ancestor of most of the cryptographic machines of the last fifty years. Like many great inventions, his device is relatively simple. And like some other great innovations, it was invented by another man. (See FIG. 21A.)

Thomas Jefferson was occupied with many subjects other than government. He invented the speedometer and a cipher machine similar to that of Bazeries. Although the idea mouldered in his papers for over a century, Jefferson's inspiration had antedated the Frenchman's by a hundred years.

The Bazeries cylinder, as it is called, consists of a number of disks and a frame. (See PHOTO 8, a homemade Bazeries

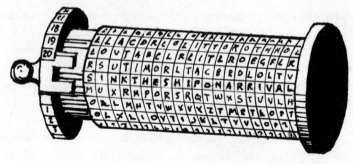

FIG. 21A. *The Bazeries cylinder*

cylinder.) Each disk is numbered on its flat side, as a hole in its center, and is inscribed with a mixed alphabet around its rim. Most Bazeries cylinders have twenty disks, but the one in the photograph, which we constructed, has only seventeen.

The frame allows the disks to be threaded on a shaft and

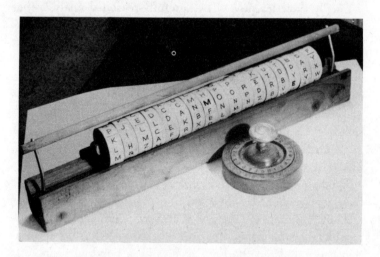

PHOTO 8. *Homemade Bazeries cylinder and cipher wheel. A message can be read on one line of the Bazeries cylinder.*

locked into place by the nut at the end. The disks can be assembled in whatever order the key requires. This key may be any sequence of the twenty numbers from one to twenty— 3-7-19-10-1-6-14-15-20-17-2-4-5-13-8-11-12-9-18-16. Since it is virtually impossible for the average person to commit such a list to memory, and unwise to write it down, a long key word or key phrase of twenty letters usually is used instead. If the key is, say, CRYPTOGRAPHIC MACHINE, the number sequence follows the alphabetic order of the letters as they appear:

C	R	Y	P	T	O	G	R	A	P	H	I	C		M	A	C	H	I	N	E
3	17	20	15	19	14	7	18	1	16	8	10	4		12	2	5	9	11	13	6

The first letter of the alphabet is A. Thus, the first A in the key phrase becomes No. 1. The second A in the key is No. 2. There are no B's and the first C is designated No. 3, *et cetera*.

With the disks spread out in numerical order in front of him, the cryptographer picks out disk No. 3 and slides it onto the shaft. Disk No. 17 comes next, then No. 20, and so on, until all the disks are in their proper order. Then the cryptographer slips the left-hand disk (No. 3) into a locked position and locates K, the first letter of the plain text on its rim. He then twirls the second disk (No. 17) until he finds I, the second letter of the message, and sets it next to the first letter. The process is repeated until twenty letters of the message can be read in order. The illustration shows a seventeen-disk Bazeries cylinder set with the message KILL DAN MOORE TODAY. The cylinder in FIG. 21A has the message SINK THE SHIP ON ARRIVAL.

Any of the other twenty-five rows produced on the machine may be used as the cipher text! In the PHOTO 8 cylinder, LHMCE KBFNN PDRBY . . . would serve, but so would the rows beginning PJEDC. . . , MQZAF. . . , QRCEA. . . , *et cetera*, around the cylinder. If the message is longer than twenty letters, the process is repeated as many times as may be necessary.

In order to decipher a Bazeries message, the cryptographer must place the disks in the correct order, and lock the cipher text into position from one end to the other. The cryptographer then revolves the cylinder, scanning each line, until he finds a row that contains the message.

In the Bazeries cylinder, the message produced is no longer than the plain text. Keys may be memorized easily and changed frequently, and while the cycle is usually fixed at twenty letters, anyone who tries to break messages in this system must solve not for one alphabetic sequence, as in Vigenère, but for twenty different ones.

Like all secret-writing systems, the Bazeries has its faults. It is much too compromising an object for a spy to carry around in his pocket, and, since a cylinder will sooner or later be captured by the enemy, the cryptanalysts probably will have to solve only the keys as they are changed.

It is not difficult to make a Bazeries cryptograph, or cipher machine. While it lacks the refinements of the locking mechanism, a homemade device can be assembled with wooden disks and a long screw. (See PHOTO 8.) First, you drill a cylindrical piece of wood through its exact center (the drill should be slightly smaller than the screw). Then the cylinder is sliced evenly, preferably with a power saw, into equal disks. Any convenient number of disks may be used (there is nothing sacred about Bazeries' twenty). Strips of paper of the exact circumference of the wooden disks must then be marked off into twenty-six spaces each, mixed alphabets written into the spaces, and the strips glued to the rims of the disks.

The Bazeries principle proved to be so useful, that it served as the basis for most of the cipher machines constructed in the fifty years following its invention. Cipher machines employing this basic idea have been used by armies and navies, by spies, by the various diplomatic corps, and by businessmen. The better machines include a number of improvements. One such commercial machine, though small enough to fit into your pocket, prints its cipher text on a strip of paper. Larger power-driven machines employ a keyboard similar to that of a typewriter. The cipher text is printed or, in some cases, even transmitted automatically. The disks are sometimes furnished in sets, so that a whole new series of alphabets may be used, with the same or different keys. (See FIG. 22.)

FIG. 22. *Electro-cryptograph*

One of the more sophisticated cipher machines that the Americans used in World War II is the telecrypton. (See FIG. 22A for picture of a similar unclassified machine.) It produces two identical punched tapes, which are turned up by an elegant electronic version of the roulette wheel. One tape

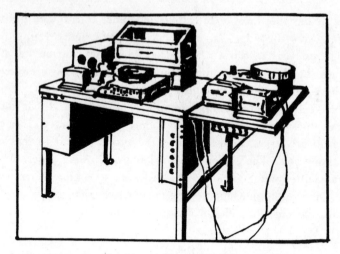

FIG. 22A. *Printing telegraph cipher machine*

scrambles the message at the sending end; the other unscrambles it at the receiving end. A danger in using the telecrypton is that the courier carrying the duplicate tape to the receiving machine might permit someone to copy it.

While serving in the OSS, Dan Moore avoided this hazard by writing his name in cobalt chloride (invisible) ink against the side of the rolled-up tape, much as a student might write his name on the outer edges of a textbook's pages. The secret ink could be developed by merely placing the tape roll, edge down, on a radiator. The heat brings out the signature quickly. If the tape were ever unrolled and copied in transit by the enemy, never again could it be rolled up accurately, with all its edges touching, and thereby recreating the signature. When the secret ink was developed, the agent knew that as long as the signature appeared in sharp detail, no one had tampered with the roll of tape.

The very thought of breaking a machine cipher without a

stolen key seems impossible. It is difficult enough to pit one's mind against another's, but outwitting a machine sounds like black magic. Certainly, machine ciphers often present tremendous obstacles. Yet, there is more than one way to get around them, and, in some instances, a machine can be used to untie the knot that another machine has tied. There is also "practical cryptography." (See Chapter 9.)

In World War II, the Americans had been picking up and deciphering radio communications from the German Embassy in a neutral country. They found themselves at a loss when the Germans installed an electrical cryptographic machine and the messages suddenly became unreadable. It would have taken weeks, and perhaps months, to accumulate enough machine-made messages to enable the Americans to achieve a solution. If something were to happen to that machine, the Germans would be forced to revert to their old, insecure ciphers, which had already been cracked.

The OSS chief in the area commissioned a local bravo to sneak into the heavily-guarded embassy and blow up the electrocryptograph with a charge of nitrostarch. As the man seemed a bit hazy about his mission, the American agent instructed him to blow up the most complicated piece of machinery in the embassy code room. At enormous risk, the local hatchetman contrived to enter the embassy, sneak by the guards, and accomplish his task. In the confusion caused by the explosion, which was so loud that it rocked embassy row, he barely escaped with his life.

The next day, to the consternation of the Americans, the Germans went right on grinding out machine-ciphered messages, as if nothing had happened. Had the native bravo lied in order to collect his reward? . . . . It was revealed eventually that the man had, indeed, blown up what appeared to him to be the most complicated-looking machine in the code-room—the Germans were out one automatic electric coffee maker!

Basically, all machine ciphers of the Bazeries variety may be attacked successfully if the cryptanalysts have sufficient messages, equipment, and time. Sooner or later, by using mathematical formulae, cryptanalysts can discover messages that are enciphered with identical and keying sequence. All some cryptanalysts require is the certainty that they are dealing with some material that has been enciphered in a system and key that are identical. If they can be reasonably certain of this, they will keep picking away until the cipher falls.

It has long been a pipe dream of cryptographers to construct a "perfect" machine, one that will not only encipher messages by the Bazeries substitution principle, but re-encipher them on a transposition principle. To accomplish this, some method must be used whereby the machine can store up letters, as it is not possible to perform transposition with only one letter at a time.

The development in the last twenty years of electronic machines that accumulate data, or "remember" sequences of numbers or letters, may mean that this dream already has been fulfilled. If so, it will be the nightmare to end all nightmares for the world's cryptanalysts. In fact, the people who live in the vicinity of the National Security Agency think that there already are too many cipher and decoding machines in existence. The electronic equipment plays hob with their television reception.

20. Secret Writing Gone Wrong

On December 22, 1894, an able and intelligent captain of the French General Staff heard himself convicted of treason and sentenced to public degradation and life imprisonment. As the epaulettes were torn from his shoulders and his sword was seized and broken, he proclaimed, "I am innocent—long live France!" He then suffered filthy, steaming imprisonment in a hellhole off the coast of French Guiana in South America—Devil's Island.

The military tribunal that sentenced Captain Alfred Dreyfus found him guilty largely because of petty jealousies within the French Army. Dreyfus was a Jew. His family came from the province of Alsace, which was under German control. His handwriting resembled that found by a French counterspy in a document filched from the German Embassy. This document, called the *bordereau* (schedule) listed secret French Army papers that its author planned to turn over to Colonel von Schwarzkoppen, the German military attaché. A mobilization plan had already fallen into German hands.

The next June, Colonel Georges Picquart, newly-appointed

chief of the intelligence section, began to suspect that Dreyfus indeed had been innocent. The plans that the captain allegedly had turned over to the Germans were prepared by the Operations Division, and had not been forwarded to the Staff at the time when Dreyfus was supposed to have stolen them. Picquart dug deeper. He turned up a letter from Major Ferdinand Esterhazy of Operations to Schwarzkoppen. The handwriting of the *bordereau* looked more like Esterhazy's than it did Dreyfus's. Esterhazy, related to an ancient Austrian family, was living beyond his means and was deeply in debt. In his possession, Picquart found the key to a complicated transposition cipher of a type little-used in France, but common in the German army.

Picquart laid the evidence before the chiefs of staff. Unwilling to have the matter reopened, they ordered him to drop the investigation. He protested that he could not keep silent while such information went undisclosed.

Picquart was rewarded for his sense of honor and justice with a quick transfer to the remote interior of Tunisia, but, before leaving, he told the whole story to a leading lawyer. Colonel Henry, an intimate friend of Esterhazy's, was appointed as Picquart's successor in France.

Colonel Henry brought forward more evidence against Dreyfus—two letters purporting to be from Panizzardi, the Italian attaché (Italy and Germany were partners in the Triple Alliance) and the text of a coded telegram Panizzardi had sent to the government. The Panizzardi message had been broken by the French Army's cryptanalysts, the famous Black Chamber, and the text implicated Dreyfus.

When the affair hit the newspapers, everyone took sides for or against Dreyfus. As in the case of Pearl Harbor, many people were less concerned with his innocence than with making political capital.

In the years that followed, Picquart was court-martialed for giving classified information to a civilian, and found guilty. Esterhazy was tried and found not guilty. Finally, Dreyfus was brought back from Devil's Island and found guilty a second time, but pardoned.

It was not until July 12, 1906, that Justice prevailed, and Dreyfus's conviction was finally set aside. Esterhazy was convicted and Henry committed suicide. The Panizzardi letters were forgeries.

Had the Black Chamber erred in the analysis of the crucial telegram? Actually, the French Army cryptographers had declared at the time that it was impossible to be certain of the text of the message; it was the French Staff that had elected to accept the wrong meaning.

Panizzardi used a dictionary code, superenciphered by the addition of a series of numbers to the digits of the code groups. By cleverly allowing a message, supposedly from a spy, to fall into the Italian's hands, and analyzing the method he used to transmit the contents to Italy, the Black Chamber finally established that, far from indicating Dreyfus's guilt, the telegram proved his innocence. Dreyfus served his country well in World War I, and attained the rank of general.

If such a miscarriage of justice could occur on cryptographic evidence, how certain can anyone ever be of the real meaning of a cipher message? The answer is not easy.

It must depend on the nature of the system used.

Even the great Bazeries could not prove that the two strange number groups in the Bulonde messages really meant that the imprisoned general wore an iron mask. The Great Cipher had certain characteristics of code, and, in dealing with a code, the analyst must work patiently through hundreds of messages in an effort to establish meanings beyond any reasonable doubt. Even then, when an unusual, previously-unlisted code group appears, it may be impossible to ascertain its significance.

It may have occurred to some readers that in selecting the

plain-text line from a Bazeries cylinder, another one of the twenty-five lines might by chance read like plain text. The mathematical probability against this is fantastically high.

It is possible for a short message, enciphered with transposition, to be anagrammed into two different, but coherent, phrases. NOTHING TO REPORT contains exactly the same letters as NO REPORT TONIGHT. There is in this instance little or no difference in meaning, but there could be, as in PRESBYTERIAN and BEST IN PRAYER. The cryptographer knows the correct reading because one of the texts shows a pattern in encipherment. (See Chapter 3.)

Generally speaking, substitution ciphers with specific keys follow orderly procedure. In a sense, cryptanalysis is not unrelated to experimental science: If a second person, following the system of the person who produced the original solution, obtains the same results from the same kind of messages, the reading is the right one. Any so-called cryptographer, who rejects possible variant readings for no valid reason, is like a scientist who ignores the results of any experiments that do not accommodate his pet theories.

When the analyst insists that a given message produce a certain answer, then cryptanalysis ceases to be a science. It was thus that in the Dreyfus case, the higher-ups in the French Army undid the work of their own Black Chamber. It is thus that self-deluded people, such as the Baconians, can convince themselves that they are dealing with cryptograms where in truth none exists, or they discover the most astonishing revelations in material that yields nothing on examination by true cryptanalysts. (See Chapter 30.)

Another matter entirely is the garbling of messages, coded or clear, in the process of transmission. This can, and does, happen frequently. We know of a businessman whose wife said to him one morning as he was leaving for the city, "Darling, do let's try to see *My Fair Lady* tonight. Just send me a telegram if you can get the tickets—I'll be out most of the day, so don't try to phone." He was in luck—an agent sold him two on the aisle. Jubilantly, he telegraphed his wife, HAVE GOTTEN TICKETS. Home from her PTA meeting, she read the telegram: HAVE GOT TEN TICKETS: Hastily, she rounded up four other couples for a theater party, and they ended up by going to a movie.

The reversal of two code groups changed the life of a Nihilist agitator against the Tsarist regime in Moscow. His friends brought pressure to bear in St. Petersburg, hoping to lessen his sentence of ten years in Siberia. Alexander III's secret police headquarters telegraphed in code to the Moscow office, PARDON IMPOSSIBLE STOP TO BE SENT TO SIBERIA. Gremlins in the telegraph system must have been on the prisoner's side. They reversed the order of two words, so that the message read, PARDON STOP IMPOSSIBLE TO BE SENT TO SIBERIA.

21. Codes of the Underworld

THE story is told that in a little village in Normandy, a butcher took unusual revenge on his upstairs neighbor, a bookseller. Dubois, the butcher, was infuriated by a long series of petty grievances. At the local café, for example, Moreau, the bookseller, never lost an opportunity to make himself out as a superior being, one who dealt in things of the mind, rather than grease and blood. When Moreau discovered that, in his teens, Dubois had run away from home and led the life of a tramp for several years, the butcher was fit to be tied. Now a respectable shopkeeper, Dubois wanted nothing to interfere with the approaching marriage of his son to the daughter of a well-to-do farmer.

Moreau's sly charges of youthful escapades gave Dubois an idea. One evening, a couple of tramps knocked at Moreau's door. They demanded food and money, but refused to work for it. Moreau might have called the police, but it happened that the irascible bookseller was not on the best of terms with the local gendarmes, and the tramps looked mean, and muscular. From that time on, scarcely a week went by without similar trouble. The harassed bookseller, afraid to leave his family in the evenings, ceased to frequent the local tavern, where he had delighted in baiting Dubois. Moreau could not understand why the tramps kept coming to his door, while they left the butcher alone.

Some weeks later, Madame Moreau remarked that whenever she washed the front door, she found a curious chalk mark there, a pair of squares interlaced at diagonal corners.

It was Dubois who had put them there. Though the sign resembled a child's scribbling to the Moreau household, it was really a secret message to all passing tramps: "You can get whatever you want here by threatening the owners."

The tramps' Code which had been in use for generations, is passed on from one vagabond to another. It remained a secret until a novice bum scribbled down the symbols, with their meanings, on a scrap of paper. When he was arrested, the police found his copy of the code.

Underworld characters also use a private vocabulary for the same purpose. When outsiders catch on to the meaning of a word, such as "heist" for armed robbery, the hoodlums drop it and take up another.

A visitor to the East End of London, where the Cockneys live, is often amazed to hear conversations that sound like pure gibberish. Englishmen will tell you such conversation is heard most often within the sound of the Bow Bells of St. Mary-le-Bow Church. One American reported that he heard a Cockney say, "My trouble and strife came the top of Rome elephant's trunk from too much jack dandy. I said, 'Where are the God forbids?' The cows and kisses put her German band over her east and south and looked down at her plates of meat. 'They're in the birch broom up apples and pears at the lean and lurch,' says she."

This is an example of Cockney rhyming slang, which, centuries ago, was the secret language of the thieves in that area.

Although still used by suspicious characters for dubious business, the argot also is employed by respectable tradesmen and shopkeepers, and crops up in ordinary conversation. Its influence extends from Bow Bells throughout an area fifty miles in circumference, and it shows no sign of dying out.

Rhyming slang usually consists of a pair of substitute words that rhyme with the actual word:

"Wife" becomes "trouble and strife."

"Home" becomes "the top of Rome."

"Drunk" is transformed to "elephant's trunk."

"Brandy" is "jack dandy."

"Kids" are "God forbids."

"The missus" is "the cow and kisses."

"Hand" is "German band."

"Mouth" is "east and south," and "feet" "plates of meat."

"Room" is "birch broom."

"Stairs" becomes "apples and pears."

"The church" is "the lean and lurch."

The weird conversation related above, reads as follows: "My wife came home drunk from too much brandy. I said, 'Where are the kids?' The missus put her hand over her mouth and looked down at her feet. 'They're in the room upstairs at the church,' says she."

Peculiarly enough, rhyming slang has a special insider's slang all its own, a wrinkle that can be extraordinarily confusing to any person attempting to learn it. It is a code language with a sort of superencipherment. The Cockneys often leave out one of the words for the sake of abbreviation, and for security. It is always the second, rhyming word of the pair, that is omitted. For instance, "plates of meat" (feet) is contracted to "plates." "Tumble down the sink" (drink) is shortened to "tumble."

When the visitor to East London believes that he is finally

mastering rhyming slang, he may be shocked to hear the sentence, "Siht Knay skool ekil na ysae kram."

This an example of the "back slang" used by Cockneys of the same district. They spell the words backwards in their minds and then pronounce them as best they can. Back slang is actually a verbal form of that most simple of transposition ciphers, reversed writing.

Even back slang has its secret variants. For example, "yes" is not "sey" but "say." The expression "back slang" for some reason is "kabec genals." Some words have evolved into something quite different from the original reversed form. "Stinking," for instance, is "kennetseeno." "Person" is "nosper."

Once a visitor in Cockneyland hears a conversation in which rhyming and back slang are mixed up with another variation known as "center slang," he is ready to get his "plates of meat moving, grab his cows and kisses by the German band and get the lleh out of the area."

Although America seems to have nothing so highly developed as rhyming slang and back slang, a customer standing in front of the roulette wheel at a carnival might well hear the operator mutter something strange out of the corner of his mouth to one of the shills. The words could be "Ushpay ethay uckersay losercay." This is "pig Latin," familiar to most school children. The first consonant of each word is transposed to the end of the word. The syllable "ay" is then tacked on. The roulette operator is saying, "Push the sucker closer."

A young lady went to her aunt's office to pick up the older woman's pay check. The aunt was ill and needed the money urgently. On the way home, a robber confronted the girl, snatched her purse, and ran away. "Help! Police!" screamed the girl. A patrolman rushed to the scene. "That man stole my aunt's pay!" she gasped. "Cut the pig Latin and tell us how it happened," said the cop.

Circus and carnival roustabouts have their own code of danger signals. It is widely known that when indignant towns-people attack them in force to recover the money that the carnies have swindled from them, the roustabouts alert their defenses with the standard code-warning cry, "Hey, Rube!"

In his youth, Dan Moore was the leader of a gang of boys in Washington, D. C. This "Mintwood Street Gang" existed for two principal reasons—first, they practiced constantly and became very proficient in jiujitsu, and secondly, to the endless exasperation of those not in the gang, they could speak very rapidly in a language that sounded like this:

OOSGGLEWHAY OTOGGLEGAY OESOGGLEJAY OGGLESOGGLEGAY?

The members referred to their private language as "hog oggle." When they were all excitedly talking at once, it sounded like a bunch of boys drowning in a bathtub.

"Hog oggle" is simply pig Latin with an "oggle" thrown in. If you cannot figure out the above sentence, you will find its meaning upside down at the bottom of this page.*

Another variant of pig Latin is the "op talk" popular in the mid-eighteen fifties. As its name suggests, the syllable "op" was inserted in the middle of words. A more recent form of "double talk," as school children call it, involves the use of "ib" in the same way.

School children have plenty of innocent fun with their secret languages, but another form of secret communication around schools is anything but innocent. A certain high-school boy was a whiz at Latin, and he could wiggle his ears. The

* Who's got Joe's goggles?

Latin teacher was a gruff old man who demanded silence in the classroom, and insisted that if his students knew nothing else, they must be able to distinguish between a gerund and a gerundive. Except for Joe, the ear-wiggling prize pupil, no one in the class could. Suddenly the teacher was elated at the remarkable success of his classroom methods: When asked whether a certain construction was gerund and gerundive, each pupil answered correctly. A wiggle of Joe's left ear meant "gerund," and a wiggle of the right one "gerundive."

Some students exert more effort in devising methods of cheating than they would require to master their material. A boy attended class for an entire year with the plug of a pocket tape recorder in his ear in order to give the impression that he needed a hearing aid. It caused no concern among the staff when he appeared for his exams with the familiar little plastic plug. On these occasions, he was listening to recordings that he had made of the key information in his courses.

A girl arrived for her math exam with a large red plastic handbag and a pair of colored glasses. Whenever a problem stumped her, she would stare at the purse. Although the surface was apparently plain red plastic, through her glasses, the girl could see the formulae she had written in green ink.

The slang word "cheaters" came into use as a synonym for glasses because cardsharps use the same kind as the girl with the red purse. To them the colored glasses reveal small markings otherwise all but invisible, on the backs of opponents cards.

A stupid but popular student at Robert College, the American college in Istanbul, Turkey, was having trouble with a math examination, and the faculty was watching him like a hawk to prevent his cheating. However, his friends were equal to the occasion.

Each of them was assigned a number. Mustapha was 1, Ahmed 2, Enver 3, *et cetera*. The originator of the idea, Kemaley, was the decimal point. As soon as the exam started, the syndicate figured out the answers like a shot and began marching in formation past the window of the examination room.

The first time they went by, Enver was in the lead, followed by Mustapha, with Kemaley next, and Ahmed last. That meant that the right answer to the first problem was 31.2. The student under examination, who had barely learned to count, electrified the faculty by knocking their hardest exam for a loop with a cool 100 per cent.

The faculty realized that someone had discovered a new secret weapon. Pandemonium reigned in their councils, but no one could think of a solution, so they retired to prepared positions and waited for the next examination.

During the next exam, a young assistant professor, Jim Eels, uncovered the scheme and even worked out the numbers that had been assigned to the various members of the syndicate. He spotted the groups going by the window and became suspicious. Since Kemaley, the normal leader of the group, was the decimal point, he was usually walking behind somebody else. With only this clue, the observant Eels cracked the students' code.

A pack of cards makes a suitable vehicle for a secret message. It may be passed easily to another person. If the fifty-two cards are arranged in a certain order, the words of a secret message can be written on successive cards with invisible ink. When the pack is shuffled, the individual words are transposed in a completely random fashion. It is then passed to the receiver, and to read the message, he has only to replace the cards into their original order and develop the secret ink. Any arrangement by suit and number, or the use of a written order, is too risky, so the secret correspondents remember it by committing to memory a doggerel verse:

Kings and Queens that are now alive
Number to (2) less than six or five.
Ten one-eyed jacks who could carry a tray (3)
Ate (8) seventy-nine for (4) lunch today.

The order would then be King, Queen, 2, 6, 5, 10, Ace, Jack, 3, 8, 7, 9, and 4. A sequence in which the suits are taken can be memorized easily, and varied from message to message.

22. COBOL and Beyond

THE hard-driving president of a large manufacturing concern sent the following note to his star salesman:

(110101)	(011011)	(101001)	(101001)	(110110)
(110110)	(011011)	(011000)	(010110)	(101001)
(100111)	(101010)	(011000)	(110110)	(011100)
(110110)	(011100)	(101001)	(101000)	(010100)
(110110)	(010111)	(010100)	(111001)	(101000)

The salesman was puzzled by the message. Suddenly, he remembered the Remington Rand Univac, the thinking machine that the corporation had just added to its staff. He fumbled through the piles of papers describing the machine. Finally, he found the card shown in FIG. 23. He looked at the first numbers in parentheses (110101). He placed his pencil point on the "11" column at the top of the card and ran it down to the "olol" column. He wrote down the letter S. The letter in the next parenthesis turned out to be H, and so on, until he had completed the message—

Remington Rand Univac
DIVISION OF SPERRY RAND CORPORATION

	00	01	10	11
0000	i X / 5	r / E	t V / N	Σ V
0001	Δ 6	,	⇑ : / O	β Y / W
0010	− −	.		: / P	: '
0011	) 0	; :	) :	+ 6i '
0100	‡ 1	A	J	/ ?
0101	" 2	B	K	S
0110	# 3	C	L	T
0111	$ 4	D	M	U
1000	% 5	E	N˙	V
1001	* 6	F	O	W
1010	& 7	G	P	X
1011	' 8	H	Q	Y
1100	(9	I	R	Z
1101	' : 1	# :	$ Z :	% − :
1110	& : / C	¢ :	* : / T	= :
1111	(: / D	@ :	? M :	NOT USED 8

FIELDS
2 3
1
4

HIGH-SPEED PRINTER
Normal: prints 1 except for characters with an entry in 4 which are non-printing.
Computer Digit: prints 1 for printing characters; 4 for non-printing characters. The digit 8 prints in place of suppressed zeros.

SUPERVISORY CONTROL PRINTER
Normal: prints 1 except for characters with an entry in 3 which are non-printing. If 3 is a ; then a : is printed; if not, typewriter action occurs. 2 is upper case where different from lower.
Computer Digit: prints 1 for printing characters; 3 for non-printing.

UNITYPER
Code impulses designated by 1.

HIGH-SPEED PRINTER ACTION
@ Fast Feed Symbol 1
| Fast Feed Symbol 2
↑ Fast Feed Symbol 3
= Fast Feed Symbol 4
г Multi-Line Symbol

SUPERVISORY CONTROL PRINTER ACTION
$ Shiftlock
% Single Shift
↑ Unshift
г Carriage Return
t Tabulator

BOTH PRINTERS
i Printer Ignore
Δ Printer Space
β Breakpoint Stop
Σ Printer Stop

U1183 Rev. 1

FIG. 23

SHOOT THE COMPETITION AT DAWN

The message was written in the Binary cipher, in which the corporation's weird thinking machine did its thinking.

At the same moment, another one of the corporation's hard-driving salesmen opened his letter from the president. Out fell the punched card in FIG. 24. His puzzled reaction was the same as the first salesman's, and then he also remembered the thinking machine. He rustled through his papers and found

189

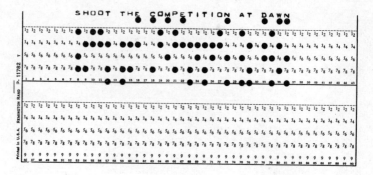

FIG. 24

the machine's punch-card cipher key. (See FIG. 25.) The first vertical column of the message, a hole; a blank, then two holes, and then a blank, turned out to be S on the key card. The salesmen wrote S at the top of the column and proceeded to work out the identical message that the first one had:

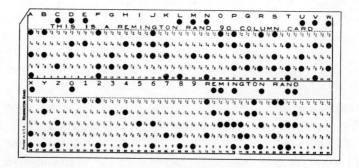

FIG. 25

SHOOT THE COMPETITION AT DAWN

A third salesman opened his letter from the president only to find a roll of perforated paper tape. He went down to the Univac room and watched the operator thread the tape into the machine. As soon as the Univac was turned on, its typewriter started clicking furiously. The salesman looked down and burst into laughter.

The corporation's polylingual machines had another type of cipher language, a magnetic tape. Its impulses could be used in a similar fashion to activate the machine's "thinking" processes.

The hard-driving corporation president was certainly joking with his star salesmen, but he was also quite serious. The corporation's thinking machines enabled them to SHOOT THE COMPETITION AT DAWN by drastically cutting costs on many of the company's most expensive operations. Not only were the conventional bookkeeping, billing, salary-paying, and other accounting functions handled by the corporation's staff of thinking machines; to a greater and greater extent, intricate metal shapes that the corporation manufactured were actually being produced by machines that were controlled by other machines instead of human beings.

Today, the intricate orders, and orders within orders, that are programmed by the codes and ciphers on the punched cards, magnetic tapes, and perforated tapes of modern cybernetic machines can actually be carried out by the machines themselves. Cipher impulses can turn an electric motor on or off, send a milling machine cutter through a complex curve, or shunt the freight cars in a terminal. The computer's arms and legs are electric currents, blasts of compressed air, and hydraulic pumps. Its eyes and vocal cords are photoelectric cells and loud-speakers. It has senses that can measure pressure, weight, temperature, humidity, and speed—and then do something about them. It has sub-assemblies that can memorize, add and subtract, multiply and divide, and even make logical deductions.

A typical machining operation is shown in PHOTO 9, in

PHOTO 9

which a pair of technicians are working out the code and cipher orders that will instruct the Univac in its job of controlling the machining of an intricate piece of metal. The Univac is sitting amiably in the background, waiting for its instructions.

In PHOTO 10, the same two technicians are watching the machine as it translates the ciphers, does the brain work, and makes the decisions in actually turning out the metal part.

PHOTO 10

In PHOTO 11, the same two technicians are examining the part to see if the machine has done its job. (It has.)

In the last two pictures, one can see the magnetic tape containing the Binary cipher that triggered the brain work.

Complicated machines are being operated by cipher-controlled mechanisms. The machines are showing better judgment, making an increasing number of decisions, developing better memories, and solving more impossible problems.

One of the authors remembers his professor in mechanical engineering at Yale, who stated that the mathematics for designing a two-arch bridge is hard enough, but figuring out the arches on a ten-arch concrete bridge, with all of the com-

193

PHOTO 11

plicated actions and reactions that travel back and forth between the arches, would require an impossible amount of
mathematical labor. In those days, it was cheaper simply to
make the bridge much safer than it had to be. Wasting concrete and labor was less expensive than mathematics of that
sort!

A modern cybernetic machine can whip out the necessary

mathematical formulae for a fifty-arch bridge without even running a temperature. In a day of code and cipher shuffling, it can easily solve a problem that would ordinarily require a thousand mathematicians working a thousand years.

A machine at Case Institute of Technology, in Cleveland, plays tic-tac-toe with visitors. (It never loses.) At the end of each game, the discouraged visitor gets a wistful message from the machine's typewriter—"How about trying another?"

At least one company is attempting to develop a machine that will take dictation like a secretary. Another machine does a reasonably good job of language translation, but has a hard time with the nuances of meaning. Another, ominously enough, seems to be able to learn by experience. It is presumably getting progressively smarter every day.

The cybernetic machines, their systems, and their uses are proliferating so rapidly (with new ciphers, codes, words, and symbols adding to the confusion) that the baffled Department of Defense called a meeting of all the manufacturers of these machines on January 7 and 8, 1960, to develop the specifications for a common, business-orientated language, COBOL, that all the machines could understand.

After innumerable conferences and discussions, manufacturers have been agreed upon the words of the COBOL system. The list will undoubtedly grow as the years go by. (See FIG. 26 for the first page of the United States Government manual of COBOL words.) Perhaps someday the Berlitz schools throughout the world will be offering courses in COBOL.

Another mathematical thinking-machine language, called "Algebraic-Oriented Language," or ALGOL, is also being developed. Every manufacturer of cybernetic machines is now working on "compilers" to translate COBOL and ALGOL into the codes and ciphers that actuate their special machines.

COMPLETE LIST OF RESERVED WORDS

The words shown below are an inherent part of the **COBOL** System. Users should avoid choosing these for data or procedure names.

ABOUT	DEFINE	INPUT-OUTPUT
ACCEPT	DEPENDING	INTO
ADD	DISPLAY	IS
ADDRESS	DIVIDE	JUSTIFIED
ADVANCING	DIVIDED	LABEL
AFTER	DIVISION	LEADING
ALL	DOLLAR	LEAVING
ALPHABETIC	ELSE	LEFT
ALPHANUMERIC	END	LESS
ALSO	ENDING	LIBRARY
ALTER	ENDING-FILE-LABEL	LINES
ALTERNATE	ENDING-TAPE-LABEL	LOCATION
AN	END-OF-FILE	LOCK
AND	END-OF-TAPE	LOW-VALUE
APPLY	ENTER	LOW-VALUES
ARE	ENVIRONMENT	MEMORY
AREA	EQUAL	MEMORY-DUMP
AREAS	EQUALS	MEMORY-DUMP-KEY
AS	ERROR	MINUS
ASSIGN	EVERY	MODE
AT	EXACTLY	MODULES
BASE	EXAMINE	MOVE
BASIC	EXCEEDS	MULTIPLE
BEFORE	EXIT	MULTIPLIED
BEGINNING	EXPONENTIATED	MULTIPLY
BEGINNING-FILE-LABEL	FD	NEGATIVE
BEGINNING-TAPE-LABEL	FOR	NO
BITS	FILE	NO-MEMORY-DUMP
BLANK	FILE-CONTROL	NOT
BLOCK	FILLER	NOTE
BLOCK-COUNT	FILLING	NUMERIC
BY	FIRST	OBJECT-COMPUTER
CHARACTERS	FLOAT	OCCURS
CHECK	FORMAT	OF
CLASS	FROM	OFF
CLOCK-UNITS	GIVING	OMITTED
CLOSE	GO	ON
COBOL	GREATER	OPEN
COMPUTE	HASHED	OPTIONAL
CONSTANT	HERE	OR
CONFIGURATION	HIGH-VALUE	OTHER
CONTAINS	HIGH-VALUES	OTHERWISE
CONTROL	I-O-CONTROL	OUTPUT
COPY	IF	PERFORM
CORRESPONDING	IN	PICTURE
DATA	INCLUDE	PLACES
DATE-WRITTEN	INPUT	PLUS

FIG. 26

Some engineers think that the final step in this line of development will be machines that are actually directed and programmed by the human voice, while all of the present ciphers, codes, and Binary arithmetical complications will be automatically taken care of by complex thinking machinery.

Univac III, a monster that rents for $22,000 per month (salary?) can handle 800,000 code signals per second. (See PHOTO 11A.) Its design was so intricate, that it had to be figured out by its predecessor, Univac I.

PHOTO 11A

At this writing, the latest wrinkle in cybernetics is the machine in PHOTO 12, the Military Digital Trainer. Its inventors, the Univac Division of the Sperry Rand Corporation, built it on the theory that the welter of codes and ciphers and other complications involved in operating thinking machines has become so complex, that the human operators will be hard-pressed to master each succeeding model. The computer in the photograph is designed primarily to train human beings in the use of its fellow computers.

PHOTO 12

If the inventors can only construct a mobile machine that will repair itself, learn from experience, build other machines like it, and purse built-in objectives, some day, mankind may wake up to find that he has created a formidable competitor on his own planet. It may be a monster competitor of such swift and subtle intelligence, that it will not only operate without man, but even supplant him as the earth's dominant thinking force.

23. Secret Inks

On the evening of April 16, 1918, American agents trailed a sixteen-year-old school girl who was carrying a folded newspaper around New York City. The girl was not under suspicion, but since one of her cousins was thought to be a German spy, everyone in the household had to be watched.

At dusk, the girl stepped into a church and knelt down to pray. She then departed, leaving her newspaper in the pew. An agent saw that another "worshiper" was present, a well-dressed older man. No sign of recognition had passed between him and the girl, but he also carried a folded newspaper as he moved to the pew where the girl had been kneeling. When he arose to leave, the agent noted that he was carrying *her* newspaper.

The agents trailed the man by taxi to Pennsylvania Station, and then by train to Long Island. He entered the fashionable Nassau Hotel, sat down in the lobby, and smoked quietly for half an hour. When he left, an agent observed that he no longer carried his paper. A few minutes later, a beautiful, elegantly-dressed blonde entered the lobby with some magazines and newspapers. After glancing through them, she arose to leave, taking the mysterious newspaper with her.

The beautiful blonde was arrested on a presidential warrant. Her newspaper contained twenty thousand dollars in pay-off money for spies and saboteurs. The lady herself, Marie von Kretschman de Victorica, one of the most famous spies in history, had been the object of a year-long search by the British secret service. She had come to the United States before America entered the war, to organize a ring of agents to cripple American factories, destroy shipping, and blow up the Panama Canal.

Evidence found in her belongings included a number of ball-point pens, which were not so common in those days, and two beautiful white silk scarves that were impregnated with secret inks. When she wished to send a message in her cipher, she had only to rinse out one of her scarves in a little water and, using this colorless fluid as invisible ink, write on rough-surfaced paper with one of the special pens. An ordinary ink message in the form of a harmless cover letter was written on the same paper, so that its lines crisscrossed those of the secret message. A special developer was needed to make the secret writing appear.

All kinds of liquids may be used as invisible inks. Almost any liquid from an animal or plant source—fruit juice or urine, for instance—will do the trick. In these cases, the only developer needed is heat. The paper is held over a lamp or candle, placed in a pan on a stove, or pressed with a hot iron. The writing then turns brown. Certain chemicals may be used in the same way. Ammonium chloride may be used to write invisible messages, which turn yellow when heated. In using heat to develop any secret ink, you must always be careful that the paper doesn't catch fire.

Specially prepared chemicals produce writing that appears

as the paper is heated, and fades away as the paper cools. The pirate's secret message in Poe's story, "The Gold Bug," was written in an ink made from cobalt oxide (the regulus of cobalt) dissolved in nitric or hydrochloric acid (spirit of niter). A cobalt-chloride solution produces blue writing with the application of heat, and the writing disappears when you breathe on it.

Other secret inks become visible only when the writing is treated with special chemicals. Ferrous sulphate, which can be purchased at drugstores and is found in chemical sets, makes a safe and effective ink when an eighth of a teaspoonful is dissolved in an ounce of water. The solution must be used immediately. In this case, the developer, or reagent, is washing soda (sodium carbonate). One teaspoonful dissolved in four ounces of water should be placed in a pan, and the message laid, face down, in the solution. The writing will appear immediately in blue, and when the paper is drying on a towel, it will turn brown. If potassium ferrocyanide is used instead of soda, the ink turns out dark blue. However, potassium ferrocyanide is a poison, and may not prove readily available.

On the night of June 14, 1942, the German submarine U-202 slipped in close to the Long Island shore to land four saboteurs in the United States. An unarmed Coast Guardsman came upon the group as they were hauling their rubber boat onto the beach. Pretending to be fishermen, they handed him a fistful of bills and told him to get lost. Returning with reinforcements, the Coast Guardsman found the beach deserted. The saboteurs had buried their equipment in the sand, caught a train to New York, and lost themselves in the crowd.

Three nights later, another load of Nazi saboteurs was put ashore twenty-five miles southwest of Jacksonville, Florida. The agents in both groups were carefully chosen and schooled by the Nazis to do maximum damage to the American war effort with a minimum of equipment. They knew that if our aluminum production could be halted for only a few hours by a single well-planned explosion in a power plant, the metal would harden and ruin equipment that could not be replaced for months.

The Nazi sabotage school specialized in instructing its operatives in carrying out their destructive mission with the simplest and most readily-available materials. These materials could be purchased, without arousing suspicion, in groceries, hardware and drug stores. An effective incendiary could be made with sulphuric acid and confectioners' sugar; a wired cork, set in a leaky pail, served as a time fuse (when the water trickled out, the cork came to rest on the bottom of the pail, completing the circuit and detonating an explosive charge). An aspirin tablet, dissolved in rubbing alcohol, provided secret ink. A bit of cotton dipped in alcohol and drawn across the paper developed the message. Who would recognize aspirin and alcohol as the tools of a spy?

This carefully-planned invasion came to naught. The chief saboteur, George John Dasch, surrendered to the FBI and made a full confession, and all the other saboteurs were promptly rounded up. They received sentences ranging from imprisonment—with eventual deportation—to death. According to the FBI, there was not a single significant case of proved German sabotage in the United States during the entire war. Times certainly had changed since 1917-18.

In World War I, spies concealed their secret-ink supplies in many ingenious ways. Maria de Victorica's silk scarves are but one example. Other agents carried their ink concentrates in socks, ties, and even cloth-covered buttons. Some concentrates were disguised as perfumes, some as mouth washes, and others as tooth pastes. The invisible-ink letters were often dipped into an ammonia solution. This made the paper a uniform off-white, and tended to disguise pen marks.

During World War I, our government searched frantically to find a substance that would develop all secret inks, until we discovered the uses of iodine vapor. The suspected letter is placed in a glass case filled with iodine vapor. The iodine which settles gradually on the sheet, shows up wherever an invisible ink has disturbed the fibers of the paper.

If iodine vapor will develop invisible writing produced by *any* liquid, it follows that plain water will serve as satisfactorily as any chemical solution for secret ink. If an overpainting with ordinary thin ink is blotted quickly, it also will reveal water messages, and the writing appears in white on the ink-covered paper.

In World War I, secret agents used many tricks to conceal the location of their invisible writing. Sometimes they wrote their messages on the upper right-hand corner of the envelope (which contained the usual "innocent" letter). Anyone looking for such a secret-ink message had to steam off the stamp to find it. Another trick was to open out the envelope and write on the inside flaps.

Yet another trick was needed to defeat the use of iodine as a universal developer. The iodine vapor works because it settles on any paper fibers that have been disturbed from their normal position; thus the spies found that they could outwit chemical detectives by dampening the whole sheet and then pressing it with a flatiron. This has the effect of realigning all the fibers so that the iodine vapor settles evenly over the whole surface. A chemical later was discovered that would develop any secret writing, with or without the dampening and pressing process.

Rarely is the routine work of spying concerned with anything so spectacular as the formula for a new explosive. Continuous and careful observation of railroads, highways, factories, and harbors provides intelligence officers with sufficient information as to troop movements and production.

In World War I, the Kaiser's counterintelligence officers were well aware that, somehow, the peasants of northern France had been smuggling detailed information about troop trains to Allied intelligence. Again and again, the counterspies carefully searched the old farm women who brought their produce into town on market days. They tore apart bunches of beets, examined baskets of eggs, and shredded cabbages leaf by leaf. The damning evidence escaped them.

The French had invented an ingenious method for concealing secret-ink messages. After carefully washing a newly-laid egg, to remove its natural coating, the spy would write his information on the shell, using one of the invisible inks that could be developed by heat. When the ink passed through the pores in the shell and was deposited on the membrane lining it, it left no detectable mark on the egg, and it was then placed in a basket with dozens of others. The farm woman who took the basket to market kept a watchful eye on the special egg, and made certain that it was sold to the right customer. The next spy in the network would peel the egg carefully, read the information on its surface, and forward it to one of his associates. He would then destroy the evidence by eating it. If the egg with the secret message fell into the wrong hands, the chances were that it would be broken and used, with no one the wiser. Only a careful hard-boiling would develop the message.

A cigarette is another favorite hiding place for short messages. The message may be written on thin paper with regular ink, or with a secret ink that does not respond to heat. It is then wrapped around the tobacco filler from a cigarette, and the original paper is replaced. This hiding place is easily destroyed. If the spy finds himself in danger, he has only to light up—being careful to apply the match to the cigarette end that contains the secret message—and after a few hard drags, the evidence is destroyed.

24. The Art of Concealment

On February 7, 1961, the British Government arrested three men and two women on charges of spying for Soviet Russia. The ring, which had been in operation for five years, had been conveying to the Reds secrets of the Underwater Weapons Research Center at Portland. These included the specifications of Royal Navy vessels and the blueprints of the nuclear sub that Britain was building with American help. At the end of their trial at the famous Old Bailey, the five received the stiffest sentences ever handed down in Britain for peacetime espionage.

Two of the agents were English—former Navy Chief Petty Officer Henry Houghton, and his fiancée, Ethel Gee, a clerk in the Portland base. Although two others called themselves Peter and Helen Kroger, and claimed to be New Zealanders, they were really Americans, Morris and Lona Cohen, former associates of the Soviet master spy, Colonel Rudolf Abel, and of the atom spies, Julius and Ethel Rosenberg. The leader of the ring passed himself off as Gordon Lonsdale, a native of Canada. Only the Soviet Secret Police know his real identity, but he is probably no Canadian and definitely not Gordon Lonsdale, although he carried Lonsdale's papers. Thirty years ago, the real Lonsdale, then eight years old, was taken to Finland by his mother. Whether he is now dead or in a slave camp in Siberia is another Russian secret. Royal Canadian Mounted Police unearthed medical records showing that he had been circumcised. The man who called himself Lonsdale was not, and is probably a Russian.

The Kroger (or Cohen) couple lived in the quiet London suburb of Ruislip, where they kept a little bookshop, and also maintained the latest in espionage devices. A thorough search of the Krogers' home revealed signal plans and key pads in the cigarette lighter on the living-room table, the most up-to-date photographic and radio devices, along with forged passports and plenty of escape money, mostly American. Kroger's study contained an excellent short-wave receiving set—with headphones—a tape-recorder that worked with the radio, and a sensitive camera together with developing supplies, for reproducing "borrowed" secret documents.

In a corner beneath the Krogers' kitchen, under the linoleum flooring beneath the refrigerator, the Special Branch officers from Scotland Yard found a trap door leading to the crawl space between the floor boards and the concrete base of the house. In the corner of the crawl space farthest from the trap door and under a pile of rubbish, they discovered a block of concrete that had recently been cemented into place.

Beneath the block was a hole two feet deep, in which Kroger had stashed his transmitter when it was not in use. Conscientious spy that he was, he apparently had cemented the cover back into place after each message to Moscow. The transmitter was no larger than a portable typewriter, but quite capable of reaching the Russian capital seventeen hundred miles away. Although it contained parts from many European countries, the completely transistorized transmitter offered no clue as to the manufacturer. This was not the sort of hardware that Her Majesty's customs officers would fail to note, and some experts believe that it had been brought into England under diplomatic immunity by an MVD officer at the Russian Embassy.

When he was ready to transmit information, Kroger would translate his message into pad cipher, using the letters as Morse code, and then play it through a speed-up device that enabled the transmitter to broadcast at three hundred words to the minute—rapid enough to defy detection. If, by chance, the British had discovered that the illicit transmission was taking place, they would not have had time to activate direction finders before Kroger was off the air. Kroger's operations were further masked by the proximity of an American Air Force base near Ruislip. No doubt, he had bought the house for its location. Since the base was on the air day and night, Kroger used a frequency close to one of those on which the base transmitted. Anyone who happened to pick up the spy messages might have assumed that he was receiving legitimate Air Force broadcasts.

For several days after the arrest, British military intelligence listened to unintelligible messages from Russia. They began with a variety of call signs, including the names of Russian rivers, place names, flowers, and stars. It seems likely that other Russian spies, still at large, also were listening in.

The radio transmitter was the most spectacular find, but the Kroger home held other secrets. In the bathroom, a can of Yardley's talcum powder seemed innocent, but someone had done a custom machine job on its top to conceal the location of a microdot reader. Whenever Kroger wanted to send his Russian masters a facsimile of one of the documents that Miss Gee had filched from the Admiralty strong room of the Portland naval base, Kroger would shrink a whole page to the size of a pinhead with his micro-camera. He then would mount the dot in an old book, usually within the elaborate capital letter at the beginning of a chapter, and "sell" the book to one of his collector friends in Europe. He would make many business trips to the Continent, carrying some of his stock with him, and he always would bring back a new supply of "rare" books. In addition to the secrets that passed from Kroger through middlemen to his bosses behind the Iron Curtain, "Lonsdale" carried on a steady correspondence with his wife in Russia through the medium of Kroger's microdots. At the time of her arrest, Mrs. Kroger was actually carrying in her handbag letters, written in Russian, to be forwarded to Galyusha "Lonsdale."

By 1960, scientists had developed a micro-micro-camera, capable of reproducing the complete Bible on an area the size of Lincoln's head on a penny. Individual letters are no larger than bacteria. Since a single speck of dust could blot out half a page, this camera may be less useful to spies than the micro-cameras that have been in use for twenty years.

Armed with a micro-camera, an agent can reproduce bulky plans rapidly and accurately and conceal his copies in such tiny items as cuff links, bolts, pens, and pencils.

In the past, a carton of brass bolts has served as a communications system. When a powerful electromagnet was held over the carton, it caused one of the bolts to jump out from among thousands of others and stick to the magnet. Unscrewed, it revealed a secret message. Although all the bolts looked alike, the one with the message was really steel, plated with brass.

In 1950, a New York newsboy received in change a nickel that felt suspiciously light to him. When he dropped it on the sidewalk, it broke in two and revealed a microfilmed cipher message. The boy turned it over to the police, who gave it to the FBI.

Hollowed coins, easy things for one spy to pass to another, were one of the tricks used by Communist agents in America that Reino Heyhanen revealed to our FBI authorities when he decided to quit working for the Reds. Heyhanen had been sent to this country masquerading as an American citizen of Estonian parentage. He signaled his arrival to his fellow spies by sticking a red thumbtack into a sign in Central Park. Soon he made contact with his boss, whom he knew only as "Mark." They met in movie theaters and crowded subway stations, and communicated by making chalk marks on a fence post in Brooklyn to indicate that messages were hidden at certain "drops" or prearranged locations in the New York area.

One of these drops was a hole in a flight of steps in Prospect Park. Park employees eventually noticed the break and filled it with cement. Years later, on Heyhanen's directions, the FBI reopened the hole and found a hollowed-out bolt concealing a tiny microfilm.

Heyhanen informed our agents that he had once accompanied "Mark" to a warehouse in Brooklyn. With this slender lead, the FBI located the building and observed everyone who arrived and departed. "Mark" was identified as a photographer who called himself "Goldfus"—and who proved to be Rudolf Ivanovich Abel, a colonel in the Soviet State Security Police.

Posing as a photographer had been a handy cover identity for the master spy. When our agents searched Abel's premises they found microdot equipment, hollowed-out articles in which to hide microfilms, cipher pads, and a powerful short-wave radio transmitter. Abel was traded for U-2 pilot Powers in a recent prisoner exchange.

The development of small and powerful radio transmitters have simplified spying activities. By sending their messages rapidly, and at irregular and prearranged times, spies may avoid discovery for months or even years. When government agents detect the sending of such messages, they try at once to spot the location of the hidden transmitter by using direction finders, the so-called D/F-ing technique. (See FIG. 27.) If two "fixes" can be made simultaneously with the revolving loop

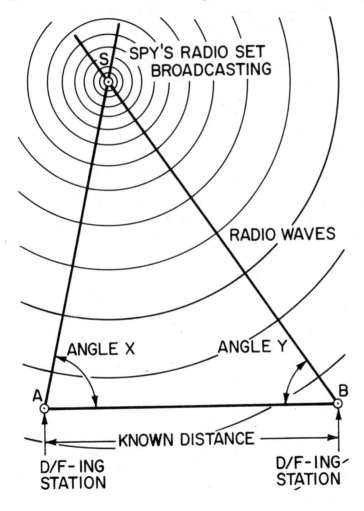

SPY'S RADIO SET
BROADCASTING

RADIO WAVES

ANGLE X

ANGLE Y

A

B

KNOWN DISTANCE

D/F- ING
STATION

D/F-ING
STATION

FIG. 27

aerials of the D/F-ing equipment, the transmitter can be pinpointed with considerable accuracy.

As any geometry or trigonometry book shows, if the base of a rectangle (the base here being the distance AB between the direction finders) is known, and straight lines are drawn from them at given angles, which are also known, then the two lines (fixes) must meet at a single point on the map. This point marks the location of the secret transmitter. By this means (triangulation), our government, in World War I, discovered the Mexican station that German agents were using to radio Berlin.

The spies had the audacity to obtain the use of the Mexican Government's most powerful transmitter, located in Chapultepec, outside Mexico City. It was strong enough to reach Berlin, and the agents' messages were sent out after the station allegedly had shut down for the night. Strong protests from the American Government, backed by the evidence produced by direction finders along our southern border, convinced the Mexican Government that it should put a stop to the illegal transmissions.

Even before our country went to war in 1917, German saboteurs were at work in America, trying to cripple our industry and shipping. Sometimes they planted aboard ships objects that resembled pencils. After a ship had put out to sea, the "pencil"—an incendiary bomb—would explode. Sometimes, violent explosives, camouflaged as pieces of coal, were dropped into the ships' coal bunkers. (PHOTO 13 shows such a piece of coal; PHOTO 14 shows the explosive concealed within it.) If the cargo was munitions, no trace of the ship or any of its crew would remain. The least that could happen would be a violent explosion in the firebox, which would explode the ship's boiler.

A pellet-hurling crossbow of the type shown in PHOTO 15 may be used to hurl a piece of explosive coal into a ship's bunkers, over the heads of the guards. In view of the fact that such a

PHOTO 13

PHOTO 14

weapon is noiseless and can shoot a piece of coal over a hundred yards from a rooftop in the dead of night, it is extremely difficult to guard against. The same type of crossbow is used for delivering coded messages. The message is placed inside a clay or plaster-of-Paris pellet and shot into an open window a block or two away. The pellet smashes against the wall, and the message drops to the floor. Note the peep sight that provides the weapon with its extraordinary accuracy.

213

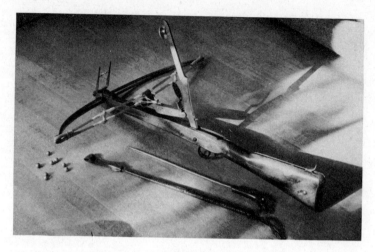

PHOTO 15

On July 30, 1916, German saboteurs blew up the Lehigh Railroad docks in New Jersey, doing tremendous damage and killing two people. The saboteurs planned this operation, known as the Black Tom Explosion, through a series of secret messages concealed in magazines. A spy pinpricked the words or letters he needed in a magazine, and then sent it to one of his partners in international crime. The articles themselves provided the cover text. After the war, the United States was able to demonstrate before an international court what had happened. Because the two countries were not at war in 1916, the United States was awarded damages amounting to twenty-two million dollars.

Pinprick messages were nothing new. In England, before the "penny post" for letters went into effect, only newspapers could be sent cheaply. People took advantage of this by mailing newspapers to each other in which dots had been placed over words in the texts to spell out messages.

During World War II, many an American soldier overseas tried to tell his wife where he was stationed by mailing home a map of the world with a pinprick through the location. Military censors became so accustomed to dealing with this violation of security that they made a habit of examining all maps enclosed in letters. If he detected a pinprick, the censor simply threw the map away before passing the letter, or else, if he had a sense of humor, added a number of pinpricks of his own. You can imagine the confusion of the poor army wife.

The number of ways in which a secret message can be written or concealed is almost endless. In the early days of the thirteenth century, a slave arrived at the court of the Mongol conqueror, Genghis Khan, at Karakorum on the Gobi Desert. According to instructions, he requested that his head be shaved. When this was done, the great Khan found that a message had been inscribed on the slave's bare scalp with a fire pencil. Throughout the hundreds of miles he traveled, no one suspected that the slave was carrying an urgent request, from his master, the Shah of Khaarisim, for military assistance. This letter helped bring about the Mongol invasion of the Middle East and of eastern Europe.

A more conventional method of concealment is shown in PHOTO 16. When pried open with a fingernail, the ring reveals a cipher message on the strip of rolled-up paper. This same type of ring has often been used to slip poison or knockout drops into an enemy's drink. Some female spies became so proficient with their rings that they could actually flip a quick-dissolving poison into a man's drink as they were handing it to him across the table.

PHOTO 17 shows another concealment device, the one fashioned from a man's belt. Some of these belts are so cleverly constructed that the message cannot be found until the belt has been nearly shredded. The tiny gun in the foreground of the

PHOTO 16

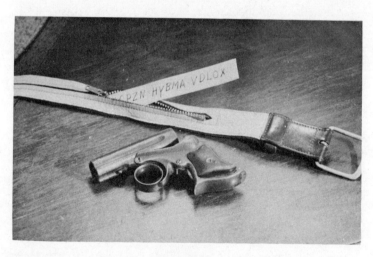

PHOTO 17

photo is the five-barreled derringer used by Dan Moore in his counterintelligence activities in Cairo in World War II.

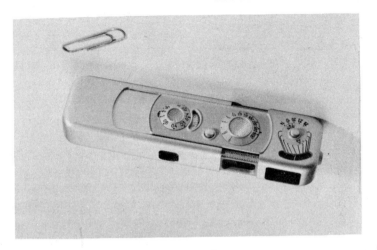

PHOTO 18

The right camera can conceal a coded communication. PHOTO 18 shows the Minox camera used by spies all over the world. It has its own built-in and coupled light meter and carries a 9.5-millimeter Doku-Ortho film strip which will take fifty extraordinarily clear pictures. A fifty-page code book, which might be dangerous for a spy to carry, can be photographed with this camera and the strip is so small that it can be concealed in a belt or a bracelet or fastened to the leg of a carrier pigeon.

Cipher messages between members of the same espionage apparatus are often concealed and passed back and forth in "camouflages." PHOTO 19 shows such a concealment device, a hollowed-out field stone. The agent thrusts the cipher message into the opening, which he then conceals with an ordinary piece of modeling clay or plasticine. He sprinkles dirt over the plasticine and drops the rock in a predetermined place. Another agent comes along, picks it up, removes the message and perhaps substitutes one of his own.

PHOTO 19

Everyone who sends and receives messages with camouflages is apt to be nervous. Many a spy has picked up his camouflage and detonated the land mine under it. One of the safest assassination devices ever invented is the other fellow's camouflage. If a spy apparatus captures one of a pair who use a camouflage, they can always get the other member of the team by booby-trapping it. No one ever picks up a camouflage when someone is looking, so there are never any witnesses to foul play.

An Egyptian herdsman picked up one of the very realistic camel-dung camouflages that the OSS constructed from plastic and tossed it into his fireplace. (Dung is a primary source of fuel in Egypt, which has no coal and no forests.) The enormous flame that resulted drove his family pell-mell from their house, and they are still wondering what their camel ate for breakfast that morning.

While we are reviewing some of the offbeat types of cipher

transmission, concealment, and construction, we should mention the powerful monarch who used a private code for a very private matter. The Sultan Ibrahim, who ruled the Turkish Empire in the mid-seventeenth century, classified the hundreds of women in his harem by a complex perfume code whereby each wife wore the perfume that would recall her to the olfactory sense.

It is said that whenever Sultan Ibrahim summoned the court perfumer, with his myriads of bottles, almost immediately he could identify any woman whose company he had once enjoyed, and whom he wanted to see again. He could identify her even if he had forgotten her name completely—as he usually did.

You can leave a secret message on an ordinary windowpane by writing on it with your finger. There is usually enough natural moisture and warmth in the skin to form scarcely visible traces on the hard, cold surface. To read this type of message, the receiver breathes on the window to cloud it over. The message then appears briefly, and fades out as the moisture dries. Or you can erase the words completely by wiping the window with a cloth.

25. The Secret Ear

In 1944, the grim Nazi prison of Flossenbürg received a new and unusual inmate. He was none other than Admiral Wilhelm Canaris, until recently the chief of German armed forces intelligence.

Like several high-ranking officers of the old school, he deplored the horrors of Naziism. He had feuded bitterly with the Gestapo chiefs, Heydrich and Himmler, who tried to establish Nazi supremacy over the military establishment. The fate of the anti-Nazi German leaders had been determined by the ill-fated bomb plot against Hitler.

When Canaris arrived at Flossenbürg, he was imprisoned, as befitted one of his rank, in the central bunker. Unlike the barracks surrounding it, where prisoners slept side by side on huge wooden shelves, the bunker held only solitary cells. Except for his trial and questioning, Canaris was kept in chains.

It might be assumed that the important prisoners, in their single cells, had no knowledge of what was going on in the prison. Quite the contrary, some of them knew at least as much as their guards.

In the next room to Canaris was another ex-military intelligence chief, Lieutenant Colonel H. H. Lunding, late of the Danish General Staff. The prison had been built hastily, and the door of Lunding's cell was made of green wood. In time, it warped, and the Dane found that he could see through the opening crack not only the corridor, but also, through a window opposite his door, the prison courtyard. Day after day, he could, if he chose to, look up from his assigned task of darning sweaters, and witness executions. Nearly one hundred men a month died in the courtyard while Lunding was a prisoner.

Lunding was able to obtain some special considerations from his guard, mostly by bribing the man with anything that had not been looted from the food packages sent to him by Danish friends. When Lunding recognized Canaris as he was led past his cell into the next one, he persuaded the guard to carry a letter to the Admiral.

Lunding might well have been expected to hate Canaris as a leader of the country that had invaded his beloved land, but actually he respected his fellow prisoner as a man who had done all he could to lessen Gestapo terrorism in Denmark. Canaris replied to the letter, but guardedly, saying merely that he was innocent of the charges against him.

Lunding then tried tapping to him in Morse Code on the wall separating their cells. Canaris, a former naval officer and intelligence chief, must have learned Morse Code at some time in his career, but he had forgotten it completely. By chance, the two men found themselves in the corridor together, Lunding on his way out for a brief exercise period, and Canaris en route for another session of Gestapo interrogation. Lunding managed to suggest that they could communicate by means of a simple tapping cipher. In this cipher, the alphabet, less the letter J, is divided into five groups of five letters each. A given letter may be expressed by two short groups of taps, the first indicating the group, and the second the position of the letter within the group. Thus A is tap—tap, or . . , B is . . . , C is . . ., and so forth to Z (. . . . .).

With a little experience, the two prisoners developed considerable facility in their strange cipher. They also became fast friends. It was to Lunding, his former enemy, that Canaris entrusted his last messages to his wife before the Gestapo dragged him out into the courtyard and put him to death. The little Admiral's last message started with the pathetic sentence, "Have been badly mistreated, nose broken."

In World War I, Germany was completely cut off from its African colonies by the Allied blockade. The old codes and ciphers that the colonial officers had used had been broken by British cryptanalysts.

Suddenly, all intelligible radio traffic between Germany and its colonies ceased, and Allied intercept stations picked up nothing but shrill squeaks. They recorded the high-pitched screams in the hope that somehow someone could make sense of them.

A British cryptographer wound up his old-style record player, listened intently to the record, which made no sense, and finally dozed off, exhausted. Suddenly, he awoke to find that the phonograph was running down, and was playing recognizable dots and dashes. The Germans were transmitting regular messages at terrific speed. The receiver had only to take down the shrill jumble and play it slowly in order to obtain the cipher text. Since the communications proved to be in the old, insecure systems, the British soon were reading all the messages between Berlin and its orphan colonies.

In World War II, jargon code was used widely to indicate the names of ships or air units. An enemy could not only listen in, but, presumably, break into a circuit with confusing or contradictory orders. Therefore, the code names were chosen to mask real identities as well as to prevent their misuse by an enemy. Thus, in the Pacific, the Americans selected names like Tillie the Toiler, with many *l* sounds. Had a strange voice come through ordering "Tirrie the Toiruh" there is no l in Japanese) to a new location, the Americans would have known at once that a Jap was breaking in on their circuit.

To keep the enemy's nose out of their business, American "Talk Between Ships," or TBS, circuits were of high frequency and short range. Under freak weather conditions, they sometimes carried farther than planned, but usually, TBS was safe from enemy ears.

On one occasion, when visual recognition signals were fouled up, TBS came to the rescue. In November, 1942, during the great naval battle of Guadalcanal, the Japanese sent in two battleships to lay down a heavy bombardment of the U.S. First Marine Division, which was struggling against terrible odds to secure a beachhead. The Americans fought back, using all of the out-gunned cruisers and destroyers available. Admiral Halsey ordered Admiral "Ching Chung" Lee to hasten to Guadalcanal with the *Washington* and the *North Carolina,* the only American battleships within thousands of miles.

Approaching Lunga Point in gathering darkness, Lee was challenged by an American PT-boat squadron. The recognition procedure had been altered, and Lee's signals looked highly suspicious to the mosquito-fleet skippers. They figured that the only battleships in the area must be Japanese. They discussed their next move by voice radio. It would be suicidal for such small craft to make torpedo runs against battleships, but if the enemy was about to enter Lunga roadstead, they had no choice but to use their "fish" as best they could.

On TBS, Admiral Lee could hear the squadron commander ordering his boats into position for attack. He broke into their circuit by calling out, "This here is Ching Chung Lee—now don't you put those fish in me!" This may not have been orthodox recognition procedure, but the sound of the Admiral's voice and the use of his Navy nickname were good enough for the PT boats. With the Battle of Guadalcanal still to be won, tragedy was averted. Another night of fighting saw the Japanese lose both their battleships and their troop-laden transports. The beachhead had been saved by a slang code, made up on the spot by a fast-thinking Admiral.

The intercepting of radio communications involves the use of receiving equipment. Over the past twenty-five years, it has been common practice to use recording equipment so that communications can be studied at leisure. Anyone dealing in "cloak and dagger" business needs a short course in the planting and detection of hidden microphones.

In 1941, hidden microphones came into the life of one Al Blake. Following a hitch in the United States Navy, Blake became a well-known actor and entertainer. He could control his muscles so perfectly that he sometimes posed in store windows along with the clothing dummies. Passers-by were urged to see if they could pick out the living man from among the plaster models. Blake also could impersonate the rigid motion of a mechanical man so well, that he earned the title of King of the Robots. Although he had been successful in silent movies, such as Charlie Chaplin's "Shoulder Arms," by 1940, he was operating a sideshow at the San Francisco World's Fair.

One day, a well-dressed Japanese stopped by Blake's concession and remarked that it was a pity Blake was not still in the Navy because he could make a lot of money if he were. Blake recognized the Japanese as Torzichi Kono, formerly Charlie Chaplin's valet. Puzzled by the remark, and by Kono's obvious affluence, Blake later tried to find the Japanese, but discovered no trace of him until March of 1941, when the two men chanced to meet on Santa Monica Boulevard in Hollywood. Blake remarked that he was thinking of rejoining the Navy. When Kono showed marked interest, the actor invented a good friend aboard the battleship *Pennsylvania* who could help in expediting the affair. At once, Kono set a date for another meeting and began to ply Blake with questions.

A luncheon with Kono led to a rendezvous on Sunset Boulevard with the Japanese master spy, Itaru Tachibaka. Al Blake was a loyal American, with no intention of betraying his country, but he was already so deeply involved in international intrigue, that it was well-nigh impossible for him to get in touch with the American authorities. If he did so openly, he could expect to be knifed in the back by Kono and company. Blake found himself followed by Japanese agents night and day. It was hopeless to try to call the FBI or the Office of Naval Intelligence. He was smart enough to realize that the Japs had planted a microphone beside his telephone.

Finally, Kono instructed him to go to Hawaii, where the *Pennsylvania* was based. Blake knew that he must act at once. If Kono were to discover that Blake's old pal "Jimmie" was imaginary, it would be the end of everything.

On a sudden inspiration, Blake went to a movie. His constant shadows were taking no chances on missing him when he came out—they had parked their cars across from the entrance and had settled down for a long wait. Blake sought out the manager of the theater, who was glad enough to do the actor a good turn by letting him escape through a side door.

He hastened to the Office of Naval Intelligence and laid his cards on the table. The ONI men asked him to play along with the Japs, and promised him that by the time he reached Hawaii, there would be a Jimmie Campbell on the *Pennsylvania*. To give Blake and "Campbell" more time, Pan American was tipped off not to sell any further space on the next flight to Honolulu. Blake got back to the theater before the feature was over. His patient shadows, none the wiser, picked him up as he emerged.

Soon, a Japanese slipped a steamship ticket into Blake's pocket. He was afraid that his friends at ONI expected him to catch a later ship, but he dared not miss the sailing. On board, he was watched day and night by a pair of Japanese, who followed him around the deck, and by a pair of Germans, who never let him out of sight in the dining salon and bar. Even if Naval Intelligence had succeeded in planting a contact with him on the ship, how could he find the man, and, having found him, talk with him in private?

Among the other passengers were the Horners, a Midwestern hardware dealer and his wife. Mr. Horner haunted the bar, drinking almost constantly. Instead of making him sociable, alcohol only increased his natural irascibility, and he argued over everything with anyone in sight. One evening, he took offense at one of Blake's remarks and lunged at him. Horner slipped and fell flat on his face, apparently out cold. Mrs. Horner put up a fuss and drafted Blake to help carry her husband to their stateroom.

When she hustled off to find the ship's doctor, Horner suddenly came to. Hastily and quietly, he gave Blake his instructions from ONI. "Jimmie Campbell" was aboard the *Pennsylvania*, awaiting Blake's call to join his "old shipmate" at his hotel. Before the doctor arrived, Horner gave Blake a final warning: "Beware of dictaphones."

Al Blake played his part so well that the Japanese never suspected that, at all times, he was working for our government. He found the microphone hidden in his hotel room and at their first meeting, indicated its location to "Campbell." His four shadows were undoubtedly listening in from adjacent rooms. Blake's efforts to lure his "old shipmate" into selling information to Japan should have won him an Academy Award. As it was, over a period of several weeks, the ONI fed carefully-doctored information to the Japanese through Blake.

Hidden microphones are often referred to as "bugs" and with the electronic developments of recent years, the term has become more appropriate than ever. Bugs today are literally no bigger than insects. Like spies' cameras and their tiny films, hidden mikes have become so miniaturized as almost to defy detection. Gone are the cumbersome, telltale wires of the years before World War II. A transistorized bug, combined with a transmitter no larger than a pack of cigarettes, can relay a "secret" conversation to an ever-listening enemy. The bugs may lie inches deep in walls, in mattresses, or in cars, and remain in operation for as long as two years, without requiring any servicing.

In Iron Curtain countries, American diplomats, their staffs, and families, are subject to continuous Communist eavesdropping. Although they may locate and remove dozens of tiny mikes, others soon take their places. Every maid, chauffeur, gardener, electrician, plumber, or repairman around an embassy is likely to be a Red agent, with plenty of opportunity to plant bugs.

A reflector of any sort may be used as a microphone—when a beam of infrared (invisible) light is aimed at it, the vibrations caused by human voices modulate the light waves bouncing off the reflector. The return beam of infrared light impinges on a photo electric cell outside the room, and the vibrating current reproduces the voices.

In 1960, Henry Cabot Lodge, U. S. Ambassador to the United Nations, exhibited to the Security Council a tiny reflector that had been installed in a plaque of the Great Seal in the United

States Embassy in Moscow. Actually, any slightly-oscillating object may be converted into a microphone by an infrared beam. Even an empty glass or a metal lampshade will do in a pinch.

No telephone conversations in Communist countries are private. The Russians make no bones about this. One operator explained to an indignant American that his call would have to be delayed because the tape recorder was out of order. An innocent-appearing telephone resting in its cradle may contain a mike, which functions whether or not the phone is in use.

When this book's co-author Dan Moore was in the Middle East as president of an export-import company, he became so incensed by a certain country's scratchy telephone-tapping methods, which made long-distance calls almost unintelligible, that he went to the secret police chief. The officer, impressed, immediately bought twenty-seven recording machines from the author. They took down conversations by induction, with no telltale scratching. After they had been installed, both the secret police and the users of telephones were much happier.

How do diplomats of the free world conduct any conversations at all behind the Iron Curtain? Even gossip about the personalities of fellow workers might give the Communists material for blackmail, so various methods of insuring privacy have been tried. Today, equipment for screening out background noise is so effective that it is no longer safe for non-Communists to mutter at each other while playing a phonograph at full volume, flushing a toilet, or jangling their keys on a glass tabletop. The West German representatives in Moscow have a special steel room with electronic safeguards against any known eavesdropping technique. It is a bug-proof chamber with built-in insecticide.

Another possibility is to speak guardedly, using some sort of jargon code. Pig Latin in any of its variants has too little security to protect conversation from Red listeners-in. Diplomats are always wise to refrain from mentioning names. Even if they use code names, such as "Joe" and "Mike" for sources of information, the Russians might figure out the informants' true identities by comparing dozens of recorded conversations—another game of "Teakettle."

The safest policy of all is to say nothing. Western representatives sometimes sit together in an inner room, "talking" over their problems by writing on scraps of paper, which they burn as soon as the message is conveyed. Since it is possible to see the traces of writing on an incinerated sheet, the ashes must then be ground to powders, for the maid who will tidy the room next morning is probably an agent of the secret police.

For the past generation, secret phone conversations in the free world have been safeguarded from potential wire-tappers by the use of "scrambling" devices. The scrambler performs a transposition process on the spoken syllables. The scrambled version of a conversation in English sounds vaguely like English, with characteristic sounds like "th", but without the unscrambler at the other end, the message is unintelligible. Scrambled speech is really enciphered speech, and with enough material, a phonic cryptanalyst presumably could break it.

26. The Secret Eye

On Tuesday, May 28, 1940, the British Third Grenadiers were holding a key sector of the Ypres-Comines line against the invading Nazis. If the Germans could break through, they would smash the perimeter behind which the Allies were withdrawing to Dunkirk, and a third of a million of Hitler's enemies would be forced to surrender or die.

Repeatedly the Germans attacked. Captain Stanton Starkey of the Grenadiers observed that his methodical enemies began each assault in the same way. First, the commander of the German ground troops would fire a pattern of red-and-white Very rockets, a code signaling a heavy mortar barrage on the British lines. Then a different Very-light signal would call a halt to the mortars so that the German assault troops could surge forward.

Time and again, the Third Grenadiers withstood the German attacks, but they were running low on ammunition. When they opened their last box, they discovered that it contained nothing but Very rockets! Captain Starkey had an inspiration. When the next barrage stopped, and the German ground forces began to advance, he fired a pattern of white-and-red signals, the German signal to commerce firing. Obediently, the German mortars opened up, lobbing their shells into their own charging troops. The German commander signaled frantically with his lights for the guns to stop. When they did, Starkey let go another fire order. Utterly confused, and badly shot up, the German ground troops withdrew for the rest of the day, and the Allies maintained their defensive perimeter. With heroism and a knack for improvisation, the British ultimately were able to rescue more than three hundred thousand men from Dunkirk.

The sun's rays, reflected in a mirror, can signal information for miles. Thus the Greeks sent word from their ships to Sinon, their spy in Troy, that it was time to open the trap door in the wooden horse.

America was once betrayed by a mirror. On the morning of the Japanese attack on Pearl Harbor, two American intelligence officers noticed a bright light flashing from the attic window of a little house perched on a cliff above Pearl Harbor. A third man joined them as they hastened to what proved to be the week-end cottage of Dr. Bernard Julius Otto Kuehn. In the hall, ready for flight, were suitcases stuffed to bursting with wads of money.

While one of the officers stood guard over Fraü Kuehn and her thirteen-year-old son Hans in the living room, the other two hurried up to the attic, where they surprised the doctor and his daughter Ruth. She was standing at the window, binoculars focused on the carnage below, calmly reporting bomb hits on American ships to her father, who would relay the information by mirror code to the Japanese Vice-Consul Otojiro Okudo. It was Dr. Kuehn's signaling that the Americans had seen. Meanwhile, on the other side of town, Okudo was translating the light flashes to a radio operator, who tapped out the information to the Japanese carrier fleet.

This nest of spies had been in operation for six years. Although the Japanese Secret Service had requested espionage aid from Germany, they were unaware that Dr. Kuehn was a member of Hitler's Gestapo. When the four Kuehns arrived in Hawaii in 1935, the doctor fostered the impression that he was a good anti-Nazi who had fled from the Reich, and that he was much interested in the early history of the Islands and in Oriental languages. Ruth, his beautiful 18-year-old daughter had been Goebbels' mistress and her older brother had been his secretary. The family was obviously well off, having received some seventy thousand dollars through a bank in Holland. American business friends of the Kuehns thought that it was clever of them, indeed, to have been able to liquidate their assets in Germany and get their money out under Hitler's nose.

In 1939, the Kuehns moved to Pearl Harbor. It surprised no one that the doctor should take the long walks with his little son Hans. Not infrequently, these walks took them to the harbor, where the Pacific Fleet was based. What was more natural than that Hans should be interested in seeing the great ships stationed there, or that friendly American sailors should sometimes invite the boy to come aboard? Dr. Kuehn himself always declined such invitations on the grounds that it was improper for an alien to accept. Everything he did allayed suspicion, but his bright-eyed and curious son saw and remembered a great deal.

Mrs. Kuehn seemed to be the traditional German *Hausfrau*, with no interests outside her home and family. However, on two occasions she made trips to Japan, serving as a courier for the Japanese secret service.

Meanwhile, Ruth Kuehn, who led a busy social life, opened

a beauty shop, ostensibly to keep herself busy. Until she ordered the best equipment from the States, and hired a competent staff for her new business venture, no really first-class salon had existed in Pearl Harbor. Navy wives flocked to her establishment. There is something about having one's hair done that releases a woman's inhibitions. All sorts of Navy scuttlebutt passed to and fro from the dryers and into the ears of the attractive proprietress. The Nazis received copies of all the intelligence the Kuehns uncovered.

As the threat of war drew closer, Dr. Kuehn abandoned all direct contact with his Japanese superiors. It was then that he and Okudo devised their simple code of mirror flashes, indicating the movements of U. S. naval vessels. They also agreed on symbols for such expressions as "direct bomb hit." on December 2, they tested their system, and found that it worked satisfactorily.

On the same day that the Japanese attacked Pearl Harbor, they also launched an assault against Guam. With most of the Pacific Fleet out of action, the Americans were unable to reinforce the few hundred men stranded on Guam, and in a few days, nearly all of them were killed or captured.

Radioman First Class George R. Tweed took to the hills, and, with the help of the native Chamorros, who risked their lives daily to provide him with food and hiding places, he remained at large. For a few months, he was able to operate a radio and to issue a one-page underground newspaper. To his friends on Guam, he was living proof that the Americans would return.

On June 11, 1944, while hiding out in a crevasse of the cliffs above Agana, Tweed heard the roar of U. S. planes, and five days later, he saw ships moving in fom the north. Suddenly, they opened fire against the Japanese installations on the island. The American Navy had come back.

Digging into his supplies, Tweed got out a large oblong section of gauze bandage. He improvised semaphore flags by cutting the cloth into two two-foot square pieces and attaching them to sticks. Signaling by flags, once a common practice, had long been superseded by searchlight signals, radio, talk-between-ships, and other methods. Tweed suddenly realized that, although he had once learned the semaphore alphabet as part of his training, he had forgotten all but the first seven letters. Racking his brains, he recalled five more, then another seven. A good signalman often has to deal with garbled messages, and if only he could attract attention, the United States Navy might be able to fill in the rest and understand his urgent call.

Day after day, Tweed waved his flags frantically, hoping that someone on an American ship would see him. Exhausted as he was from two and a half years of exposure and semi-starvation, he could signal for only about twenty minutes at a time.

Again and again, he watched a pair of destroyers circle the island. On July 10, they came close to shore—too close, Tweed thought, for he knew that there was a concealed battery of big Japanese guns at Adelup Point. The Jap gunners held their fire deliberately, waiting for the landing.

It was late afternoon when the two destroyers came within two miles of the shore, and the light of the setting sun inspired Tweed with a new plan. He climbed to the very top of the cliff, carrying his flags and a three-inch pocket mirror. Catching the sun's rays, he reflected them directly at the bridge of one of the ships. When he was certain that someone must see the light, he snatched up his flags and waved them wildly. Then he spelled out, "Please answer by searchlight."

A searchlight from the bridge winked "K", the code for "Go ahead!"

Tweed was too wise to try to identify himself—that would have been a spy's first move. Instead, he warned the destroyers of the hidden guns, and informed them that the Japanese were killing any American pilots who fell into their hands.

For half an hour, the destroyers circled slowly nearby, receiving all the dope that Tweed could relay concerning Japanese strength, offshore barriers, mine fields, and dummy guns. When at last he saw the ships putting on speed to leave, Tweed, with tears running down his cheeks, asked if they could take him aboard. One of the ships lowered a boat, and he warned the Navy that it would take him half an hour to reach the shore. He gathered his gear and raced down the cliff in record time. The boat remained offshore half a mile away. Tweed signaled with a flashlight, directing the crew to a landing, but they were wary of a trap. At last, the exhausted Robinson Crusoe of Guam swam out to the boat, and his countrymen joyously pulled him aboard.

Food, hot showers, promotion, interrogation, and back pay followed. If Tweed had not used his mirror, he would not have been able to get his vital information to Admiral Turner's staff before the landing. If he had gone on flashing with the mirror instead of using his flags, he would have been killed on the spot, for when they first saw the flashes of light at the top of the cliff, the Americans had mistaken them for Japanese guns opening fire.

Light does not have to be visible for communications. The human eye sees a limited range of the electromagnetic radiation we call light—only the familiar spectrum of red-orange-yellow-green-blue-violet. Light of a higher (ultraviolet) or of a lower (infrared) frequency is invisible. In World War II, the following exchange became popular among cloak-and-dagger men:

> "What are the colors of the OSS?"
> Answer: "Ultraviolet and infrared."

A ship's blinker can be fitted with a special filter to absorb all the wave lengths of light except infrared. Another ship can "see" the invisible coded messages transmitted in infrared rays by means of heat-sensitive equipment or photoelectric cells. Certain light-sensitive substances, such as those in your light meter, produce a slight current whenever light—visible or invisible—strikes their cells.

By the end of World War II, light was being used extensively for secret communication, by land as well as by sea. Light has one tremendous advantage over radio in military communications: the enemy cannot intercept messages by simply tuning in on a given wave length and standing by. To intercept a light message, you not only need the proper equipment but you must know exactly where and when to look. Light travels over short distances in a straight line, and no eavesdropping enemy, sitting behind a hill, can expect to pick up a secret light message.

In 1960, the invention of the light mazer was announced. For the first time it was possible to transmit numerous electrical impulses simultaneously and to amplify the intensity of light. With the light mazer, it is theoretically possible to send and unscramble patterns of light. Within a matter of years, we should be able to bounce light messages off artificial satellites to any spot on earth. And some day, we will use areas on the moon as if they were giant screens, reflecting thousands of messages at once.

27. Tales of the Pacific

In the early days of the Pacific war, the Coast Watchers of Australia were recruited from the "islanders," planters, traders, and civil servants who lived in the areas mandated to Australia —the Solomons, Papua, New Britain, and New Ireland. These hardly Australians were well known to the natives, without whose help they could not have survived behind Japanese lines. They had been quickly trained in the use of codes and ciphers, and they were equipped with radio transmitters, receivers, and code books. While some of the radios were unmanageable affairs, requiring the help of a dozen native bearers for every move, the best were compact little devices, no larger than breadboxes, originally designed for the use of airborne doctors whose patients were scattered over hundreds of square miles in Australia's "outback" interior. These efficient little machines had a voice range up to one hundred miles, and could carry code and cipher up to three hundred miles.

In the jungle regions, where so much of the Pacific war had to be fought, it was no easy task to keep alive. It was even harder to maintain radio communications. Transmissions travel farthest after nightfall, the time when the jungle often is lashed with rain. In those transistorless days, the sets had to be operated with cumbersome batteries, subject to tropical mold and constantly in need of recharging by gasoline engines. The Coast Watcher had to remember the location of buried fuel supplies, and when all else failed, men actually distilled a combustible fluid from palm juice.

In addition to all these minor difficulties, a Coast Watcher fulfilled his mission in the very jaws of death. At any moment, a Japanese patrol, following the fix of a radio direction finder, or pursuing the lead of a bribed or tortured native, might push through the jungle to seize a lone "Aussie." His life was often a nightmare of hasty encoding and transmission, sudden warning, hurriedly destroyed code books, malnutrition, tropical disease, and long jungle treks one jump ahead of his pursuers. Sometimes the Japanese patrol actually outdistanced its quarry, and the watcher found himself one jump behind.

For a long time, the Coast Watchers were the only eyes for the Allied forces in the Southwest Pacific area. Their reports on Japanese plane and ship movements provided the slim margin for victory in the photo-finish battles of 1942-1943.

Early in 1942, at Southwest Pacific Headquarters in Australia, the Allied Intelligence Bureau was established, thus incorporating all the information-gathering resources operating in an area almost as big as the North American continent. Augmenting the Australian Coast Watchers, the new organization brought together Americans, British, Dutch, and Filipinos. In addition to obtaining specific information about the movements of Japanese air and sea forces, and the exact location of military targets, the Allied Intelligence Bureau tested the loyalty of the people in Japanese occupied territories. The Bureau also contacted whatever scattered guerrilla units were opposing the Japanese, and rescued civilians and military personnel trapped behind enemy lines.

The Bureau had to re-equip and supply the "stay behind" agents, who were given full military status, to send in men to take the places of the sick and wounded, and to operate watching posts in areas where the Allies had no eyes. That was a tall order.

On New Guinea, the Japanese recovered parts of a Coast Watcher's code book. The Allied Intelligence Bureau developed new and more secure cryptographic systems to take the place of those that had been discovered. Many of them were ciphers devised by a gifted Tasmanian school teacher. The Bureau also sent into the Philippines a special group of agents, provided with new ciphers and adequate radios. This "Operation Planet" was headed by Captain Jesus Villamor, a Filipino who was already an air hero.

Before boarding the submarine *Gudgeon,* which was to take his party to the islands, Villamor carefully trained and equipped them. The new cipher systems were reduced to microfilms, one of which was sewn behind the ankle patch on an old pair of sneakers. Another required special dental work— it was secreted in one of Villamor's teeth. The *Gudgeon* also carried medicines and surgical supplies, emergency rations, and cigarettes. Everything was sealed into watertight containers, with every spare corner stuffed with wadded-up pages from American newspapers and magazines. The very packaging was information to sustain the morale of Filipinos who had listened to nothing but Japanese propaganda.

The Planet party landed on the central Philippine island of Cebu. When one of their three rubber rafts proved unusable, Villamor was forced to leave everything on the sub except equipment absolutely vital for his mission—money, radio, and ciphers.

The party was met by one of the many competing groups of guerrilla irregulars. (In addition to the big war, half a dozen private ones were in progress among rival leaders.)

Villamor's scarred face was familiar throughout the islands, and, in time, he was able to weld the disorganized guerrilla bands into a disciplined fighting force. He carefully refrained from establishing radio contact with the Brisbane headquarters until his position was secure.

Almost at once, Villamor discovered treasure trove. From a beached vessel, some of the guerrillas recovered what appeared to be a Japanese naval code book. Villamor instructed one of his most reliable men to carry it to the southern island of Mindanao for a secret rendezvous with an American submarine. Experts at Brisbane, MacArthur's Australian headquarters, could hardly believe their luck.

That was the first Japanese naval code book to be captured in the war. It turned out to be enormously valuable, not only for decrypting intercepted Japanese messages, but also for explaining the nature of enemy communications.

Cryptanalysts cherish any clues concerning the probable wording of unreadable messages and the mental patterns of enemy cryptographers. That captured code book, together with a further document from Cebu, (see page —) determined to a large extent the outcome of the greatest naval engagement of the war, the battle for Leyte Gulf.

In May, 1944, a courier arrived at a secret American post on the Island of Samar with word that his leader, whom he identified as Andy Anderson, needed medical supplies and ammunition, and could supply important information. The message was relayed by radio to Colonel Allison Ind in Australia. Although he recognized the name as that of a comrade-in-arms during the defense of Bataan, he had to be certain.

If the man really was Anderson, he alone could answer certain questions. The next night Ind contacted him on the air waves. "What did we call the pet monkey?" and "What was the hobby of the BOQ cook?"

Twenty-four hours later, Ind got his answer—"Tojo" and

"woodcarving." These single-word replies not only identified Anderson, but also served as the key words for a cipher system in which further communication was carried on.

This new contact in the Philippines provided information from a previously "dark" sector, and also rescued Americans who had been hiding out for two years. It was not until the end of the war that Ind learned from Anderson that the rumor of Villamor's activities had prompted him to undertake the risky task of making contact with the Bureau.

One of Villamor's triumphs was the smuggling of an entire communications system into Manila. The transmitter was broken down into the tiniest of component parts, and each one of them was then embedded in a vegetable or fruit. Castañega, the agent entrusted with this strange load, committed to memory both the circuit for the radio and the entire cipher system to be used with its messages. He ferried the baskets of camotes, corn, cocoanuts, and potatoes across heavily-patrolled waters and transferred them to native carts, which passed through enemy roadblocks.

In time, the vegetables and fruits, minus the hardware, were sold and eaten, perhaps by Japanese officers. The radio was painstakingly reassembled in the Manila home of an American, and its cipher messages brought the scattered guerrilla bands of the great northern Island of Luzon into contact with one another and with the Allied Command.

When the Allied Intelligence Bureau sent Major J. H. Phillips, a former planter from Mindanao, to Mindoro Island, just south of Manila, his landing apparently was witnessed by a wandering fruit seller. The man went straight to the headquarters of the Kempai Tai, or Japanese secret police, and sold his wares. Immediately, direction finders scanned the air waves for Phillips's transmissions.

Touched by the plight of the Filipinos under the invaders' rule, the American stayed on the air too long, broadcasting in his cipher detailed accounts of their suffering. He also did not bother to change his key words as often as his instructions specified. Because his station was on the air for such lengthy intervals, the Japanese pinpointed his location. It appears likely that the Japanese cryptographers, given such a wealth of messages, broke his cipher. In any case, the Kempai Tai struck simultaneously in three areas, mortally wounding Phillips and killing or seizing nearly all of his men.

In the years 1943-44, the network of Allied eyes in the once-blind Philippines expanded rapidly. Each week, hundreds of cipher messages from the hidden radios were picked up in Australia, and many of them carried precise information on ship movements.

American submarines supplied the Intelligence Bureau's network, and the subs' records of sunken enemy shipping soared. Stations with call signs, such as ISRM ("I shall return" —MacArthur), relayed information gathered by courageous Filipinos, some of them highly educated young men, who represented themselves as ignorant farm boys to secure laborers' jobs at Japanese installations. Their reporting was unbelievably thorough and accurate.

When a sudden flurry of naval activity in early 1944 brought to Davao certain Japanese units thought to be far from the islands, an American agent enciphered the information, and thoughtfully added to the message the words, I AM SOBER. Clearly something important was about to happen in Davao.

On April 20, the Allied Intelligence Bureau received the first of a series of bewildering garbled bilingual messages from the only man who was in a position to report on the Sulu area. Knowing their agent's habits of thought and expression, headquarters half-deciphered and half-cryptanalyzed his messages. There were evidently twenty-seven warships in the Sulu Sea!

The Bureau urged their informant to take no risks and to stay off the air until he knew in what direction the vessels were heading. At last, he broke radio silence with his own brand of plain English: DOSE GUYS ARE MOVING EAST! They were heading for the Philippine Sea, where Admiral Spruance, the victor of Midway, intercepted and defeated them.

The Bureau was able to plant a number of British agents in the East Indies. A watch on Balabac Strait, north of Borneo, reported all Japanese ships passing between Malaya and the Philippines.

Agents sent to the Island of Timor, however, simply disappeared. Finally, signals came back from one party, but the authenticating letter groups, which would have indicated that the cipher messages were actually from the British agents, were missing. Although headquarters feared that the messages came from the enemy, it could take no chances. Planes were dispatched, at great risk, to drop food and medicine. When the war ended, a final message arrived over the Timor frequency. It thanked the Bureau for the supplies and bore the signature "Nippon Army."

In the spring of 1944, there occurred a series of events so fantastic that no serious novelist would presume to incorporate them into a work of fiction. A sequence of strange coincidences became links in a chain that the Allies were able to forge into a weapon for victory. Every link, including the cryptographic one, was vital to the outcome.

Following Admiral Yamamoto's death in April, 1943, the top command of the Combined Imperial Japanese Fleet passed to his successor, Admiral Mineichi Koga. It was obvious to Koga that the Japanese, forced back from the enormous perimeter of their 1942 offensives, must hold the inner defensive line through the Philippines that protected Japan's life line to the oil-rich Indies. It was equally obvious that the Allies intended to breach that inner line.

In February, 1944, Admiral Koga went to Tokyo to complete plans for the defense of the Philippines. Practically every plane and ship that Japan could still muster—the land-based air units at Singapore, the huge battleships stationed in Japanese waters, the newly-trained forces from the home islands —were to be concentrated against the expected American assault.

With this "Z" plan, Koga returned to his fleet base in the Palau Group. At that time, Admiral Halsey's hard-hitting carrier task force was raining heavy blows in an area that had been virtually a Japanese lake for two years. Destruction fell from the skies upon Palau. The American airmen bombed shipping, wrecked every aircraft in sight, and actually laid mines around Koga's fleet anchorage.

The Japanese Commander-in-Chief decided that his head-quarters would have to be moved; it was useless to plot the defense of the Philippines from a spot that the Americans could batter at will. Koga and his staff decided that they could work more effectively from Davao, capital of the southern Philippine island of Mindanao. Since the Admiral's planes had been destroyed, three big four-motored Kawanishi flying boats were ordered from the Marianas to Palau. One of them may have developed engine trouble; in any event, only two arrived.

On the evening of March 31, Admiral Koga prepared to leave. For security, Vice-Admiral Shegeru Fukudome, Koga's chief of staff and second in command, was assigned, with half of the staff, to one plane, while Koga, with the rest of the staff, was to occupy the other.

Suddenly the air-raid alarm sounded. Koga, who was in no mood to wait for another visit from the Americans, embarked immediately and ordered the pilot to take off. The air alert proved to be a phony, but Fukudome, who had orders to confer with his chief upon his arrival at Davao, followed him a few minutes later. In those few minutes, his pilot received a warning that a typhoon lay squarely across the eight-hundred-mile route to Davao. Fukudome ordered his pilot to fly northward, around the storm.

Fukudome assumed that Koga's pilot had received the same warning on his radio, but apparently he had not. It seems probable that the first Kawanishi, carrying the commander of the combined Imperial Japanese Fleet, flew due west, straight for Davao and directly into the typhoon. No trace of the plane or any of its occupants was ever found.

Admiral Fukudome carried the detailed, written version of plan "Z," on which the future of the Japanese Empire depended. With the plans were code sheets, indicating exactly the ships or units, the tactics and the commanders referred to in cryptic references of the master document.

The plane flew high to escape the typhoon's fury. The lack of oxygen made some of the passengers drowsy, and the fuel ran low. Having gone nearly six hundred miles north off his course, the pilot requested the Admiral's permission to land at Cavite, on the big northern Philippine island of Luzon, in order to refuel.

Mindful of the scheduled conference, and not knowing that Admiral Koga was dead, Admiral Fukudome ordered the pilot to proceed southward. If necessary, the plane could put down at one of the many Japanese installations in the islands.

When the flying boat was in the vicinity of Cebu or of Bohol, in the central Philippines, the pilot calculated that they were still nearly two hundred miles from their destination. It would be necessary to land at Cebu City, so the pilot dropped down to get exact bearings, and Fukudome recognized the tall chimney of the Asano cement factory.

Suddenly, the horizon cut off the moon's light, and tropical night engulfed the flying boat. When the pilot was unable to regain altitude, the plane stalled and sideslipped into the dark waters. Ten passengers, including Admiral Fukudome, struggled loose from the wreck before it burst into flames.

The Admiral had heard tales that Cebu was a hotbed of anti-Japanese guerrilla activity, but he hoped that the small rescue boats putting out from shore would be Japanese craft from the naval base. Instead, they were Filipino fishing vessels from the coastal village of Balud.

The ten Japanese, all of them injured and half naked, were hauled aboard and carried ashore. Admiral Fukudome, who still clutched his brief case, lost consciousness. When he recovered, true to the Samurai code, he tried to encourage his unfriendly Filipino captors to shoot him and the rest of his party. Many of the guerrilla guards were willing, but cooler heads recognized the value of living captives.

The Filipinos set out for the secret headquarters of their guerrilla chief, James Cushing, an American who had come to the Philippines long before the war, as a mining engineer. Cushing was in scarcely better shape than Fukudome. Thin and exhausted from the rigors of his hunted existence, he was so ill from malaria that he could walk only with the aid of crutches. For weeks and months, he had been the object of relentless Japanese search parties. Somehow, with the devoted help of the Filipinos, he had kept himself, his clandestine radio, and his precious ciphers out of enemy hands.

Admiral Fukudome and his men resolutely ignored the questions fired at them by their captors, until one of Cushing's men addressed them in Japanese. Eventually, most of the prisoners admitted that they knew English, but the Admiral absolutely refused to disclose his true identity.

Despite the condition of his uniform and personal papers, Cushing and the Filipinos realized that he must be a high-ranking officer. Was he a general from the Macassar area? Or perhaps an Admiral? In time, the guerrillas came to believe that their prisoner was none other than Admiral Koga. Since the Commander-in-Chief had vanished without trace, the best-informed men on both sides might have believed the same thing.

The prisoners were given the poor best that Cushing's hide-out could offer in the way of food and medical care, and, before long, the Japanese military command on Cebu began to scour the island for the missing officers.

If there was excitement on Cebu, MacArthur's headquarters in Australia was in an uproar over the news. It was quickly arranged, by ciphered radio messages, that three of Cushing's most trusted men were to carry Admiral Fukudome's brief case across Cebu—a difficult jungle operation even without the frantic Japanese patrols—and then by boat to Negros, for a secret rendezvous with an American submarine. With enemies in hot pursuit, the three reached their destination at almost the very moment the undersea craft surfaced. The couriers delivered the brief case, then melted into the jungle, and the sub slipped back under the water minutes before the Japanese came upon the site. Soon the sub was racing to Australia with one of the most important cargoes of the war.

Cushing was ordered by radio to hold the prisoners at all costs. Meanwhile, an elite Japanese marine unit was rushed to Cebu. Cushing, with some of his prisoners still on stretchers, took to the bush with the few remaining guerrillas and sought temporary refuge in a last-ditch defensive perimeter.

The Japanese colonel in charge of Cebu proposed that throughout the island, which compares in area and population with the State of Rhode Island, every man, woman, and child should be put to death—unless the prisoners were set free immediately. Behind his feeble defenses, Cushing held a private consultation with Admiral Fukudome. They drew up a document offering the release of the prisoners if the Japanese army, in its turn, would agree to a temporary armistice. The

American was so exhausted and ill that he had to make two attempts before he could sign his name to the paper.

The Japanese colonel agreed. An unarmed detachment of Filipinos carried the prisoners to the lines of their compatriots. Would the Japanese commander keep his word, accept Admiral Fukudome's pledge, and put an end to the killing? He did, and Cebu enjoyed a three-day armistice.

Meanwhile, the brief case reached Australia. All the documents were carefully photographed, and, as the interpreters set to work eagerly on the copies, the originals were loaded back into the case and rushed by submarine to the site of the crash. The Allies hoped that by leaving the papers for a Japanese diver to find, they might trick the Nips into thinking that the "Z" plan and its key had never fallen into American hands at all.

This clever trick unfortunately did not work. The Japanese realized their loss, no doubt from Admiral Fukudome's statements after his release, and fired another ultimatum at Cushing. When he failed to produce the brief case, Cebu was subjected to savage bombing and strafing. Nevertheless, when the Americans took the island late in 1944, Cushing himself was on hand to greet them.

The value of Admiral Fukudome's brief case, even after the Japanese knew that it had been captured, was incalculable. The strategic and tactical plans might be altered, but the Japanese could scarcely change the nature of the land, sea, and air forces explicitly detailed in the meticulously coded pages. Nor could they at that late date replace some of the additional codes and ciphers that had been broken by the information in the brief case. When MacArthur was ready to return, his naval and air commanders knew exactly what they could expect, where they could exploit weaknesses, and what they would need to oppose strength with greater strength.

28. Some Unsolved Mysteries

MANY bits and pieces of parchment were found in the cave of the Dead Sea Scrolls, or in other caves in the vicinity. And to complicate matters further, some of the Dead Sea Scroll material was in cipher. In some cases, the cipher is simply reversed writing; in other instances, substitution appears.

When the scholars wearied of handling, cleaning, and matching the bits of parchment, they organized a contest to see who could break the substitution cipher first. The system employed a number of alphabets, not the precursors of the Vigenère alphabets, but rather four sets of phonetic symbols—the Latin, Greek, Phoenician, and Aramaic alphabets. While other scholars struggled to set up frequency tables, the winner cracked the messages by intuitively guessing the identity of one long word with a characteristic letter pattern.

Other ancient cryptograms have proved harder to break. In 1912, a New York dealer bought a chest of old manuscripts in Italy. One of them, which became known as the Voynich Manuscript, a bound book eight-by-six trim size, was in an unknown cipher. Although many scholars and cryptanalysts have tried to make sense from it, no one has succeeded.

About forty years ago, a professor claimed to have solved it through a series of complicated steps involving both substitution and transposition. Working from the strange illustrations, he interpreted the work as proof that Roger Bacon was the greatest genius in history—not only had he invented the telescope and microscope four hundred years before their time, but he had discovered astronomical and biological facts supposedly unknown until the twentieth century.

Unfortunately, this "solution" depends on an irregular transposition, which does not come out the same way twice. The world has had six hundred years to read this Voynich Manuscript, but its real meaning, if any, is still unknown.

It is well known that pairs of any sort can be grouped to represent letters of the alphabet. Thus the dot and dash, or short and long sounds or strokes, make up Morse Code. Sir Francis Bacon conceived the idea of concealing a cipher message in any printed text by dividing the cover text into groups of five letters each, and using two kinds of type. The casual reader, not suspecting that the cover text contained any hidden meaning, would simply assume that the printer had been careless. On the other hand, the reader who was in on the secret, would divide the text into groups of five letters, designating one kind of type "a" and the other "b"; he could then read the cryptogram from a substitution table. Such a secret message requires five letters of cover for each letter of message, and anyone suspecting the nature of the cipher need have no trouble in solving it. The biliteral cipher is a special kind of simple substitution; its security depends entirely on the ruse that it does not resemble secret writing.

Bacon set up his equivalents as follows ("a" is the first type face; "b" is the second):

A	aaaaa	I-J	abaaa	R	baaaa
B	aaaab	K	abaab	S	baaab
C	aaaba	L	ababa	T	baaba
D	aaabb	M	ababb	U-V	baabb
E	aabaa	N	abbaa	W	baaba
F	aabab	O	abbab	X	babab
G	aabba	P	abbba	Y	babba
H	aabbb	Q	abbbb	Z	babbb

If someone wanted to write the name BACON in the biliteral cipher, using any line from Shakespeare as the cover, it could appear as follows:

Plain text: B   A   C   O   N
Cipher equivalent: aaaab   aaaaa   aaaba   abbab   abbaa

Biliteral
form: aa aa b/a aaa a/a aa ba/ab ba b/ab baa/
Cover text: to be *o* r not t o be *th* a*t* *is* *t* he *q*ue stion

The more similar the two type faces are, while still distinguishable, the more secure this type of cipher is. Most of the Baconian arguments revolve around the question of whether or not there are two or more type faces in a given document. One Bacon enthusiast "broke" an original Shakespeare folio on the basis of a biliteral cipher. When the letters were photographed and shown to him separately, it was found that he could not really distinguish separate type faces; he had let his imagination run away with him.

There is no reason why a biliteral cipher should be restricted to printed matter. The effect of two fonts of type can be obtained in a handwritten cover text. The b's for instance, may be retraced in a heavier manner, ending in downstrokes instead of upstrokes, or simply signaled by the presence of small dotts or pinpricks over or under them.

The Nihilist Substitution, by which Mikhailoff smuggled instructions for the assassination of Tsar Alexander II through the hands of Melikoff's secret police, (See Chapter 4.) was a biliteral cipher. Having solved the transposition, the police thought that they were in possession of the secret message, but it was only the cover text. The Tsar-Liberator was blown up, and Russia started on the path to revolution, because of a perfectly understandable cryptanalytic oversight.

Whole words, rather than letters, may be the basis for Baconian five-symbol substitution. The a's can be words beginning wtih consonants, while the b's are those that begin with vowels. Indeed, there is no reason why the biliteral effect must depend on written matter at all.

In World War I, eighty members of the army cryptographic outfit lined themselves up for a picture. Those facing the camera directly were a's while those who turned their heads aside were b's. Divided into groups of five, the eighty faces made sixteen letters. They spelled out the message KNOWL-EDGE IS POWER.

Since Francis Bacon applied the system to printed matter, Baconian cipher detectives usually turn to print. One group of Baconians devoted themselves to examining the first complete printed edition of Shakespeare's work, in the hope of finding a hidden message. At least two kinds of type were used in the First Folio. Fantastic revelations have been claimed as the result of these researches.

After their many years of distinguished government service, the Friedmans (See Chapter 16.) brought their accumulated cryptographic wisdom to the study of the alleged Shakespeare ciphers. They demonstrated beyond doubt that none of the messages "discovered" ever existed.

Type was so expensive in the seventeenth century that printers habitually combined anything usable from an old set with a new one. Therefore, the presence of more than one variety of type is meaningless. The almost imperceptible differences really involve not two, but several fonts. Different copies of Shakespeare's works show bewildering variations.

Baconians have worked out different meanings for pages that are really identical, and identical readings for those that are really different. The Friedmans demonstrated the mathematical impossibility of other ciphers that misguided or self-deluded Baconians have brought forward. "Cryptograms" in the wording of the poet's collected works and on his tomb display the same basic lack of sound rules and specific keys. The "authorship" of Edward de Vere, Earl of Oxford, is likewise easily disproved. Employing the same methods of elaborate and irregular transposition, dear to the Baconians and Oxfordians, the Friedmans "proved" that the real author of Shakespeare's works was Lewis Carroll, Gertrude Stein, Theodore Roosevelt, Mark Twain, and William Friedman, Esquire.

It is hard to believe that so many kinds of ciphers can be hidden in the same texts. As the Friedmans point out, ghost writers sometimes claim credit for their work in hidden ways. A Spaniard, Juan Lopez Cancelada, for instance, used the letters of his own name to introduce successive paragraphs of a history of New Mexico, which was published as the work of a nobleman, the Count of Torene.

Although none of the cryptographic "evidence" that Bacon wrote Shakespeare will hold water, this fact alone is no proof that he did not. Some writings have to be attacked as if they were cryptograms, even though the authors have not tried to hide their meaning. This is the case with certain ancient languages. The old languages of Persia and Egypt have been broken as if they were codes or ciphers. The problem, in fact, is much more difficult than it would be if there were any clue to the nature of the language. An unknown language expressed in an unknown alphabet presents much the same problem as a coded text with a cipher superimposed.

Some people did not believe that the hieroglyphs of ancient Egypt were writing, but presumed that they were sacred signs and symbols. The problem was simplified somewhat when an officer of Napeleon's army discovered the Rosetta stone in Egypt in 1799. It contained the same message in three languages, two of them known, and the third in unreadable hieroglyphs. When a cipher expert gets his hands on this kind of "pony"—a readable and an enciphered version of the same message—it is usually not difficult for him to analyze the general system and recover any special keys involved in the cipher. From then on, he can read anything written in that cipher. Languages are like codes, but even so, the "pony" ought to make possible the identification of all the words appearing in the text.

Many language specialists tried their hand at deciphering the Egyptian part of the Rosetta Stone and ended with the conviction that the problem was impossible. The brilliant young Frenchman, Champollion, succeeded where they failed, because he kept his mind open to suggestion. Ancient Egyptian repeats sounds in a way unlike any known language, and today, some scholars can read Egyptian hieroglyphs as accurately as any other language.

Ancient Persian had to be broken in similar fashion, though the language itself was quite different. The scholars began with words as clues, such as the names of kings, that they could reasonably expect to find. Even with probable words available, many men devoted their whole lives to the puzzle before it was solved.

The isle of Crete, sixty miles south of Greece, boasted great cities and a flourishing sea trade thirty-five hundred years ago. A few written records survived, largely by accident. Their paper turned to dust, but sometimes the Cretans wrote on wet clay, which was later dried in the sun. Wetting destroyed many such records, but a number of tablets were accidentally baked by fire, when the buildings in which they were stored burned down.

On the tablets that survived, scholars noticed two kinds of writing, in lines from left to right, to which they gave the names Linear A and Linear B. In addition, some writing was in the form of pictures. There was no clue to the nature of the language.

Michael Ventris, a young English architect with cryptographic leanings, began a detailed study of the B writings, which led to a startling conclusion. He proved beyond question that the old Cretan language was actually a form of Greek, seven hundred years older than any "ancient" Greek previously known. Unfortunately, he was killed in an automobile accident in 1956.

The languages of the Hittites, who lived in Asia Minor four thousand years ago; of the Etruscans, who ruled northern Italy before the Romans took over; and of the Mayas, of Central America, have all come down to us as code-and-cipher problems. Progress has already been made with these languages, and we can expect that the final mysteries of these secret writings will be unlocked in our time.

Another entirely new challenge in cryptography stems from the question, "Is there a code of life?" Biologists are beginning to discover that there is. Biological scientists have found that an unimaginably complex and accurate system of programming is going on all the time in the formation of living organisms. Within the nucleus of every cell are unbelievably tiny chains of chromosomes, which carry something very like coded instructions for the organism's future development. A single cell's hereditary orders may determine that it is to remain a single-celled alga, or that it is to become a red-haired, blue-eyed, male human being.

Biologists have experimented with chopping up the material in the embryo of a chick, without actually killing all the cells. When the surviving cells are placed in an environment suitable for further development, each follows its coded instructions. Scientists have reported finding that one cell, obeying its internal code, can reproduce itself to become a bit of kidney tissue, while another can form skin, and yet another a blood vessel (the creature itself does not even exist!).

Some diseases such as cancer, apparently involve a disturbance of the proper reproductive pattern of individual cells. Cancerous cells appear to be garbles of the proper biologic codes; they issue wild and contradictory orders that can ultimately kill the organism. They are like the false codes with which Admiral Hall and his Room 40 started the "diversion" on the Belgian coast, which so badly damaged the Germans. (See Chapter 9.)

When the code of life is cracked, some means may be found to filter out or short-circuit the confused, garbled, and deadly messages that cancer issues. Understanding and control of cell development will do more than bring individual diseases under control; it will give to mankind a power as awesome as that of atomic energy. By splitting the atomic nucleus, scientists released unheard-of power. By directing the splitting of a cell's nucleus, we may some day be able to invent new species of plants and animals at will, and perhaps even set our own codes to keys that will improve the human race.